# PI IN THE SKY

## Hands-on Mathematical Activities
## for Teaching Astronomy

by Robert Pethoud, M.A.

ZEPHYR PRESS
Tucson, Arizona

PI IN THE SKY
Hands-on Mathematical Activities
for Teaching Astronomy

Grades 8–12

© 1993 by Zephyr Press.
Printed in the United States of America

ISBN  0-913705-80-2

Cover Design: Michelle Gallardo
Editors: Stacey Lynn and Stacey Shropshire
Book Design and Production: Nancy Taylor

Zephyr Press
P.O. Box 13448
Tucson, Arizona 85732-3448

# CONTENTS

**Introduction** .............................................1

   Standard Supplies ...............................3
   Special Materials ...............................3
   Terminology .....................................4

**1. Astronomical Angles** ........................13

   Background .....................................13
   Preparation ....................................15
   Angles, Size, and Distance .....................16
   Body-Measured Angles ...........................17
   Cross Staff ....................................19
   Angular Size of the Sun ........................21
   Further Explorations ...........................22
   Worksheets .....................................23

**2. The Size of Earth** ..........................31

   Background .....................................31
   Preparation ....................................36
   Build Sun Compasses ............................38
   Finding True North .............................39
   Finding Your Meridian ..........................41
   Earth's Circumference ..........................44
   Further Explorations ...........................44
   Worksheets .....................................47

**3. The Moon's Size and Distance from Earth** ....49

   Background .....................................49
   Preparation ....................................52
   Relative Size and Distance .....................52
   The Moon's Phases ..............................52
   Earth's Shadow in Space ........................54
   Earth and the Moon to Scale ....................56
   Further Explorations ...........................56
   Worksheets .....................................59

## 4. The Sun's Size and Distance from Earth .......67

Background ....................................................67
Preparation ...................................................68
The Distance to the Sun ....................................68
The Size of the Sun .........................................69
Further Explorations ........................................69
Worksheets ...................................................71

## 5. The Distances to the Stars .....................77

Background ....................................................77
Preparation ...................................................78
Inverse Square Law .........................................79
Distances to the Stars ......................................79
Putting it All Together ......................................79
Our Galaxy of Stars .........................................79
Worksheets ...................................................80

## Appendixes ...........................................87

A. Glossary ...................................................87
B. Pursuing an Interest in Astronomy ...................91
C. Derivation of Formulas .................................94
D. Answer Key ...............................................98

## Bibliography .........................................111

To my father, who gave me my first telescope;
my mother, who nurtured my interest in astronomy;
and my wife and children for their love and support.

# INTRODUCTION

As I was supervising a graduation ceremony on the local high school's football field, a group of six parents approached and anxiously asked for help. The sun was near to setting and at this moment appeared to rest atop the bleachers on one side of the field. The parents queried expectantly, "We were told to sit on the west side of the field. Which is the west side?"

It is sobering to realize that such a fundamental notion as where the sun sets could escape not just one but a whole group of adults. Stories abound of citizens so ignorant of geography that they can't find their own country on a world globe. It is frightening to contemplate such people making decisions affecting themselves and others when they quite literally don't know where on Earth they are. Those ignorant of astronomy are just as handicapped, as they don't know where they are in the universe.

*Pi in the Sky* has several goals. One is for participating students to construct accurate and lasting mental images of our neighborhood in space. Specifically, they should learn the following:

- The relative sizes of Earth, its moon, and its sun
- The relative distances to the moon, the sun and other stars
- How the sun, Earth, and moon move relative to each other
- How these motions affect what we see from Earth

Because another goal of this project is for students to see how scientific knowledge is obtained, the data used in creating these mental models are to be obtained firsthand by the students using simple, homemade tools. It is exciting for students to discover, without relying on tabulated values, such data as the size of Earth and the distance to the moon, especially when the process is even more instructive than the end result.

Think of astronomy, and starry nights and telescopes may well come to mind. *Pi in the Sky* was written for teachers who have access to neither of these commodities. The activities are designed for daylight hours (except for a couple of short homework assignments) using materials commonly found in schools or, when necessary, in the local hardware store. This is in keeping with a third goal: for students to gain a sense of the unlimited potential for exploration of our world that is possible with only the simplest equipment.

In these activities, students learn how to calculate such quantities as the size of the moon and the distance to the sun. By not relying on data in books, students can experience exhilaration and power in their newfound abilities. Using the students' own abilities fulfills a final goal of the project: to enhance the students' self-images.

*Pi in the Sky* is best suited for use in grades eight to twelve, although it could be used in sixth or seventh grade with a knowledgeable, dedicated teacher and interested students. The entire series of activities should take about four weeks to complete if they are used daily in classes of 40 to 60 minutes. The actual time needed will depend on the sophistication of the students and on how many of the excursions are pursued.

For full benefit, the activities should be completed sequentially. It is possible, however, to do only one of the exercises or a subset of the entire series. For example, the circumference of Earth activity can be undertaken separately, or the first three groups of activities can be used to give a good picture of the Earth-moon system.

Students should have certain knowledge and skills before they attempt the activities in *Pi in the Sky*. A very basic knowledge of astronomy is assumed, much of which could be learned concurrently. The "Terminology" section presents more than enough of the vocabulary with which the students should become familiar. In addition, students should know that the sun is a star, that stars shine by their own light, that planets shine only by reflected light, that the moon orbits Earth, and that the Earth-moon system orbits the sun.

In the area of mathematics the students need to know the following:

- how to estimate the measures of angles in degrees
- how to measure angles with a protractor
- how to measure lengths with a metric ruler
- how to set up and simplify ratios
- how to set up and solve proportions
- how to use integer exponents
- how to evaluate square roots of whole numbers
- how to use scientific notation

- that the sum of the angles in a plane triangle is 180 degrees
- that the circumference of a circle is pi times the diameter
- how to do simple geometric constructions

Most of the materials needed to perform the activities in *Pi in the Sky* can be found in any school, but some may have to be purchased elsewhere. Below are listed the standard supplies needed and the more unusual items required for specific groups of activities:

## Standard Supplies

| | |
|---|---|
| Paper, 8 1/2" x 11" | Compasses |
| Paper, 8 1/2" x 14" | Protractors |
| Pencils | Rulers |
| Chalk | Metersticks |
| Felt markers | Hole punch |
| 3" x 5" cards | String |
| Masking tape | World globe |
| Scissors | Volleyballs |
| Straight pins | Ice cream sticks |

## Special Materials

| | |
|---|---|
| Astronomical angles: | Cardboard boxes |
| | Tinfoil |
| | Adding machine tape |
| Size of Earth: | Pine boards, 1" x 12" x 12" |
| | Circular bubble level |
| | Rubber suction cup darts |
| | Large rubber bands |
| | Light bulb and socket |
| | Conference telephone or postcards |
| | Inflatable world globes or volleyballs |
| Moon's size and distance: | Adding machine tape |
| | Small foam plastic balls |
| | Light bulb and socket |
| Sun's size and distance: | Cardboard boxes |
| Distances to the stars: | Candles |
| | Photographic light meter |
| | Box of salt |

## Terminology

Were it not for the motions of Earth, the "fixed stars" would indeed appear to be motionless. In spite of their rapid movements relative to us, the distances to them are so great that to the casual observer they appear to be quite stationary.

The most obvious motion of Earth is its spinning on its axis. This, of course, is what makes the stars and other celestial objects appear to rise in the east and set in the west. If you could hover motionless in space over the north pole, you could watch Earth turn beneath you. (1) Would it rotate clockwise or counterclockwise? (Answers are found in the Answer Key in Appendix D.)

To specify positions of celestial objects, it is convenient to think of them as being located on an enormous sphere whose center is Earth—the dome of the sky or the celestial sphere. As Earth rotates counterclockwise on its axis, to anyone on Earth looking south the celestial sphere appears to rotate clockwise (see figure 1). Extend Earth's polar axis out to this sphere to points we call the *north celestial pole,* often abbreviated NCP, and the *south celestial pole,* SCP. Project Earth's equator onto the sphere to define the *celestial equator.*

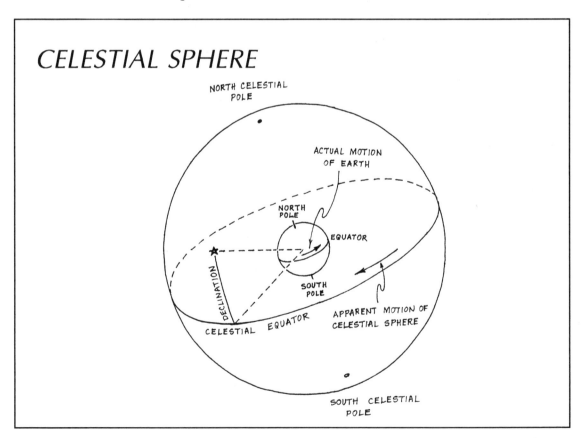

Figure 1

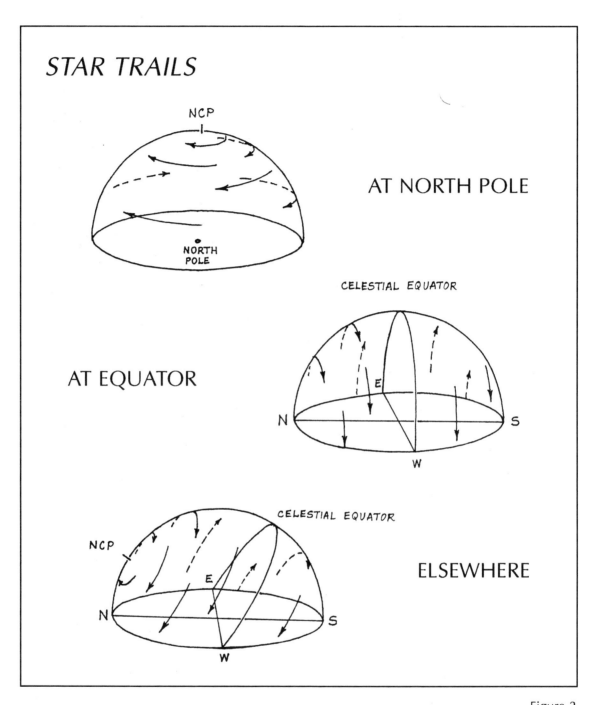

*STAR TRAILS*

AT NORTH POLE

AT EQUATOR

ELSEWHERE

Figure 2

Stars near the celestial poles are called *circumpolar* stars because, to observers far enough away from the equator, they seem to move in circular paths around the celestial pole, i.e., they do not rise or set. If you lived at the north pole, the north celestial pole would be directly overhead and all visible stars would seem to revolve around it. Stars would not rise or set at all—all visible stars would be circumpolar (see figure 2).

If you lived on the equator, the celestial poles would be found opposite each other on your horizon, and the celestial equator would run from east to west directly overhead. All the stars you could see would rise and set.

Most of us live between these extremes and therefore find the celestial pole and celestial equator neither on the horizon nor directly overhead. Your position on Earth can be described by your latitude and longitude. A line running east and west through your location, extended all the way around Earth, describes your circle of latitude. A line running north and south through your position, extended to the poles, becomes your meridian of longitude.

Notice that even though you live hundreds or thousands of miles north of Earth's equator, the celestial equator meets your horizon at the points precisely due east and due west of you. (2) If you are north of Earth's equator, why doesn't the celestial equator meet your horizon south of these points? (See figure 3.)

Your meridian of longitude, projected onto the celestial sphere, becomes your *celestial meridian* (see figure 4). Your celestial meridian extends through the north celestial pole and the point directly overhead, called your *zenith*, and meets your horizon directly north and south of you. A star or planet will be at its highest point in the sky for a given day when it crosses your meridian between the NCP and the south point of your horizon. This is important to remember.

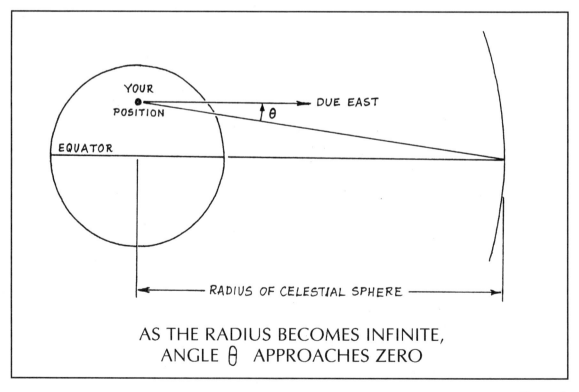

Figure 3

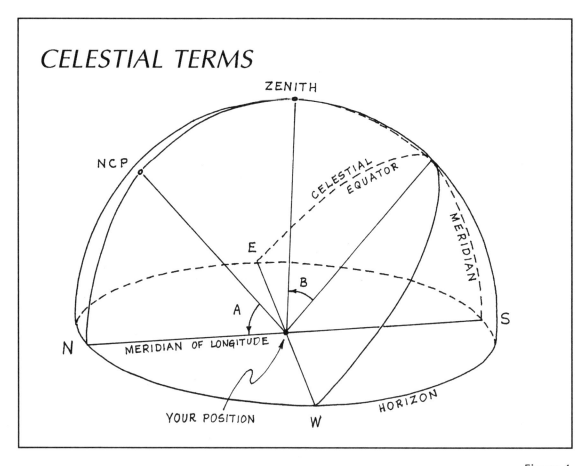

*CELESTIAL TERMS*

ZENITH

NCP

CELESTIAL EQUATOR

MERIDIAN

E

B

A

N

MERIDIAN OF LONGITUDE

S

YOUR POSITION

W

HORIZON

Figure 4

As a celestial object moves across your meridian, it is said to *transit the meridian*. Our measurement of the time of day is partly based on how close the sun is to the meridian. The actual moment of meridian transit is called *local apparent noon*. Before the sun reaches the meridian we have morning (A.M., ante meridiem, before meridian transit); after transit we have afternoon (P.M., post meridiem, after meridian passage).

Take another look at figure 4 and decide what can be said about angles A and B. What do they represent? It turns out that angle A is congruent to angle B and each of them is equal in measure to your latitude. To understand why, imagine you are standing on the deck of a ship somewhere along Earth's equator. The celestial equator runs through your zenith and the north celestial pole is on your horizon. Now sail a few degrees north of the equator. The north celestial pole will now be that same few degrees above the horizon and the celestial equator will cross your meridian the same number of degrees south of your zenith (see figure 5). The angle between a point on the sky and your zenith is called that point's *zenith angle*. The angle between the point and your horizon is its *altitude angle*. Of course, zenith angle and altitude angle of a point on the sky are complementary.

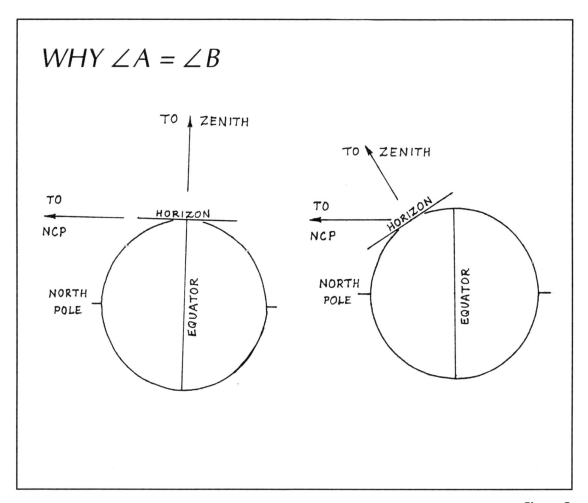

Figure 5

In the northern hemisphere we are lucky in having a bright star very near the north celestial pole. The star is Alpha Ursae Minoris, the brightest star in the constellation of the Lesser Bear. It is the star at the end of the handle of the Little Dipper. Alpha Ursae Minoris is more popularly known as the polestar, or simply Polaris. It is very easy to find this star using the so-called pointer stars of the Big Dipper, part of Ursa Major (see figure 6). An easy way to find your latitude north of the equator is to measure the altitude angle of Polaris.

Just as locations on Earth can be specified by latitude and longitude, locations on the celestial sphere can be given by the analogous quantities of declination and right ascension. Latitude on Earth is the angle between a given place and Earth's equator, measured from the center of Earth. On the dome of the sky, *declination* is the angle from a celestial object to the celestial equator, measured from Earth. (3) What is the declination of Polaris? (4) What is the declination of a star that crosses your meridian at your zenith?

Longitude on Earth is the angle between a given meridian and the prime meridian, the meridian of Greenwich. This angle can be measured in degrees or hours. (5) One hour of longitude is the same as how many degrees? The analogue of longitude on the celestial sphere is right ascension. *Right ascension* is measured in degrees or hours eastward along the celestial equator. The starting point for this measure is the First Point of Aries, or the vernal equinox, located very near the eastern side of the great square of the constellation Pegasus.

To understand the significance of this Point of Aries, we'll look at another of Earth's motions. At the same time as it rotates on its axis, Earth revolves about the sun. Earth's orbit is elliptical with an eccentricity of 0.017, so it is very nearly circular.

In figure 7, notice how Earth's axis appears tilted. The axis is not quite normal (perpendicular) to the plane of Earth's orbit. This tilt is the source of seasons in the temperate zones, as it causes the sun's rays to strike a given spot on Earth more directly at some times and more obliquely at others.

The plane of Earth's orbit is called the *ecliptic*. From the vantage point of the sun, the path Earth traces in the sky is the ecliptic. From Earth, the same plane is defined by the path the sun traces against the background of stars over the course of a year. The name "ecliptic" comes from the fact that eclipses can occur only when the moon crosses this plane.

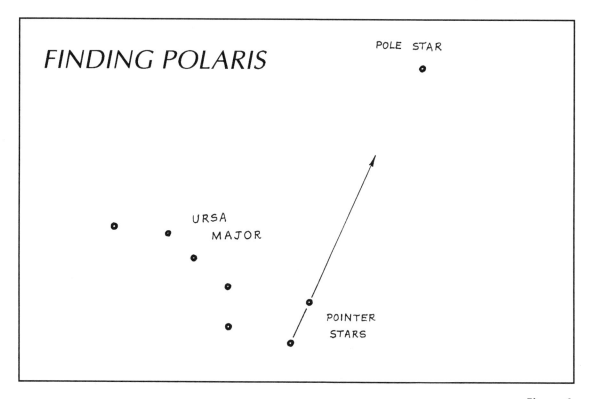

Figure 6

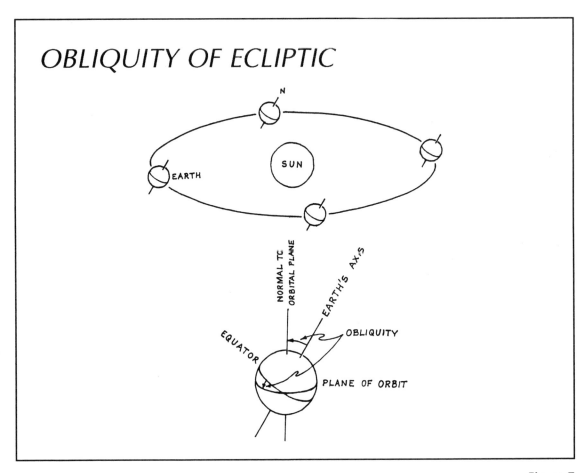

Figure 7

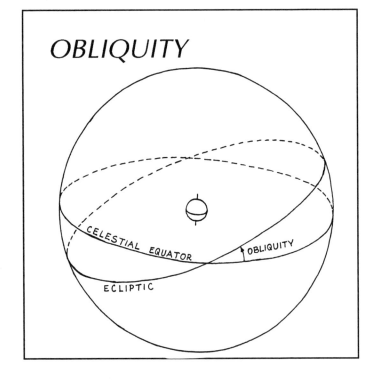

Figure 8

Projected onto the celestial sphere, the ecliptic is represented by a great circle (see figure 8). The planes of the celestial equator and the ecliptic can be seen as two different great circles on the celestial sphere. The angle between the planes of the celestial equator and the ecliptic is called the *obliquity of the ecliptic* or just the *obliquity*. Notice that this angle is also the tilt of Earth's axis with respect to the normal to the plane of its orbit. It measures about 23.5 degrees. (6) Given that the sun, if it could be seen against the stars, appears to move eastward along the ecliptic each day, does Earth move clockwise or counterclockwise in its orbit when viewed from above the north pole? (7) Roughly how far east along the ecliptic does the sun move each day?

The time when the sun reaches the point on the ecliptic farthest north of the celestial equator is called the *summer solstice* in the northern hemisphere. At this point in its orbit Earth's north pole comes closest to pointing toward the sun. Viewed from Earth, the sun's position in the sky is closest to the NCP at this time. In the temperate northern latitudes, the sun's position at noon is nearer the zenith than at any other time.

Six months later, the sun reaches the southernmost point on the ecliptic, called the *winter solstice* by us northerners. To get from one solstice, or standstill, to the other, the sun must cross the celestial equator. In September, on its way south, the sun crosses the celestial equator at a point called the *autumnal equinox*. In March, on its way north, the point of crossing is called the *vernal equinox* or spring equinox. These terms apply both to points on the celestial sphere and to the times at which the sun occupies those locations.

In the southern hemisphere the seasons are reversed, because when the north pole comes closest to pointing toward the sun, the south pole points away from it. On days when the sun passes high overhead for North Americans, its greatest altitude angle is much lower for Australians.

Many people believe that the reason it is warmer in summer than in winter is that Earth is closer to the sun in summer. Actually, the sun is about the same distance from Earth all year. The difference in seasonal temperatures has to do with the angles at which the sun's rays strike Earth's surface.

It may not be necessary to present to students all the concepts mentioned in the foregoing discussion, but you should be well versed in all of them. If any of the ideas are confusing, refer to one or more of the books listed in the basic astronomy section of the Bibliography.

# CHAPTER 1
# Astronomical Angles

This chapter demonstrates three simple tools for measuring angles on the dome of the sky. These tools are used to find your latitude and the angular diameters of the sun and moon, quantities that will be needed in later chapters.

## Background

How have astronomers pieced together our current picture of the universe? Their starting point—and ours—is familiar to all: the nightly display of pinpoints of light in the black sky. From careful observation of this spectacle they have determined that Earth is a rocky ball that spins as it revolves, in the company of other flotsam, about an unremarkable yellow star located in a spiral arm of a larger-than-average galaxy of hundreds of billions of such stars. They know that the nearest of these other stars is so far away that its distance must be measured in light years, yet they think they know how large these stars are, what they are made of, how they shine, what will happen to them, and even when they were born and when they will die.

Not being able to bring stars into the laboratory for analysis, astronomers have had to tease every possible bit of information out of simple observation. They have meticulously measured intensities, colors, and directions of starlight to get the base of data that, when combined with cleverly constructed logical arguments, has led to the current edifice of knowledge.

Before it was possible to quantitatively measure the intensities and colors of stars, early astronomers evaluated the directions to these celestial bodies by measuring angles on the dome of the sky. Even with the crude instruments of the time, by about 100 years before Christ, the Greek philosopher-scientists had rough ideas—and sometimes quite reasonable ones—of the sizes of Earth, the sun, and the moon and the distances separating them, all deduced from these astronomical angles. The ancients lacked some technology, but they developed the powerful mathematical reasoning that makes all scientific progress possible.

Schoolchildren are accustomed to measuring angles with protractors. Clearly, unless modified, such tools are not of much use for judging angles on the sky. Over the centuries, many instruments have been invented for measuring astronomical angles: astrolabe, cross staff, back staff, quadrant, octant, and sextant to name a few.

Before learning to use sophisticated tools, though, one must learn what it is one is measuring and how to estimate measurements without tools. Worksheet 1A, "Angles, Size, and Distance" (pages 23–24), is designed to get students to think about the relationship between angular size and actual size. Even a small object can subtend a large angle if it is close to the observer, and an enormous thing can subtend a tiny angle if it is sufficiently distant. The students must understand that when they measure separation angles between celestial objects they are *not* finding linear distances.

To be competent at measurement, one must be able to estimate reasonable answers even without access to a measuring tool. For example, that full-grown tree may be 30 feet high; it certainly is not 3 feet high. One goal of this chapter is for students to become good estimators of astronomical angles.

Remember that during these exercises the observer is always at the vertex of the angle he or she is measuring. Once outdoors, students should realize that the angle between the horizon and the zenith is 90 degrees, a right angle. From this, it should be easy to estimate angles of 45 degrees and even 30 degrees. Angles smaller than this present more of a challenge, but fortunately a helpful tool is readily at hand. It turns out that a hand with fingers fully spread, held at arm's length, subtends very close to a 20-degree angle. Similarly, at arm's length a fist subtends about 10 degrees and a finger about one degree. (See diagram on page 25.) Students are to discover these relationships and then use them to measure the altitude of Polaris and the angular diameter of the moon. They should also measure some other astronomical angles, such as the angular separation of given stars.

The cross staff is an ancient navigational instrument that has been obsolete for centuries. It was used to find the angular distances between celestial objects. It can be oriented to measure angles in any direction, unlike a clinometer, which can measure only altitude angles.

The cross staff that will be constructed is perhaps the simplest version conceivable, consisting of nothing more than a 3" x 5" card and a piece of string. It will be used to provide an independent measure of the moon's angular size. Students can also use it to check other astronomical angles.

To measure the angular size of the sun another method will have to be used, since one must never look directly at the sun. The image of the sun will be projected from a pinhole onto a piece of paper some distance away, and it is this image—never the sun itself—that will be observed. The sun's angular size will be found two different ways from the same image: (1) the size of the image and its distance from the pinhole will be measured and the angle found by geometry and (2) the length of time needed for the image to move by one image diameter will be measured and the angle found by comparing this time to the time needed for the sun to (apparently) move 360 degrees.

# Preparation

## Materials

Card stock, such as 3" x 5" index cards
String or thread
Cardboard boxes, about 30 cm x 30 cm x 60 cm or larger
Tinfoil
Masking tape
Scissors
Pencils
Rulers
Protractors
Hole punch for paper (optional)
Adding machine tape
Straight pins

Select one wall of your classroom to be used for displaying angles, and mark one point on this wall at about the students' eye level (see figure 1-1). This is the zero degree mark. From this mark measure perpendicular to the wall a convenient distance and indicate this spot on the floor with a cross of masking tape. This spot is where the students will stand to make their observations. Now place markers on the wall to indicate every few degrees from zero to 30 degrees as measured from the cross of tape on the floor. The distance from the zero degree mark can be found using the formula $L = D \times \tan A$, where L is the distance from the zero mark to the new mark, D is the distance from the zero mark to the cross of masking tape, and A is the angle.

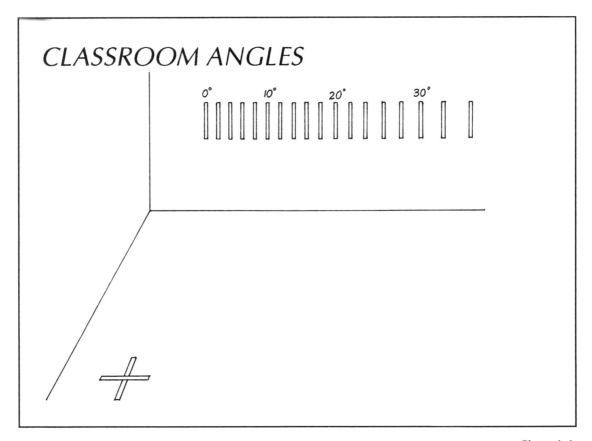

Figure 1-1

## Angles, Size, and Distance

Worksheet 1A, "Angles, Size, and Distance" (pages 23–24), should be preceded by a discussion of what angles are, how they are measured, and what they tell us about the actual sizes of objects. Even eighth-grade students who know that the angles of a plane triangle sum to a straight angle often think that a triangle of smaller linear size must have smaller angles than a larger triangle.

As with nearly all the activities in *Pi in the Sky*, this worksheet is intended to be completed by teams of two or three students working in cooperative learning groups. In my experience, these groups work best when the tasks are well defined and time limits are clearly established.

After the worksheet is completed, the groups should share their results in a whole-class discussion of what was learned. Everyone needs to know what it means for an object to *subtend* an angle for an observer and that the angle subtended by a given object gets smaller as the distance to the object increases.

## Body-Measured Angles

Before students learn how to use their own bodies to measure angles, it is a good idea for them to get some practice at estimating angles. Go outside and have the students stand so that the angular separation between two trees or the angular extent of a building is 90 degrees. Then have them move until the angle is 45 degrees. Demonstrate that the angle from zenith to horizon is 90 degrees. Challenge them to estimate the angular extent of something that you have already determined to be about 15 degrees when measured from a certain spot.

Now have the students complete worksheet 1B, "Body-Measured Angles" (page 25). One at a time, they will stand at the spot marked on the floor and use the scale on the far wall to measure the following items held at arm's length: hand with fingers spread (thumb to little finger), thumb to last knuckle of fist, and width of index finger.

Students will record their individual results on the worksheet. After they have made their personal measurements, the data can be compiled from the entire class and averages found. Interested students may wish to find the angles between index and little fingers of their hands (around 15 degrees) and between the first and second knuckles of their fists (about 2 degrees).

Have students go back outside and estimate again the angle presented to them before in the challenge. Finally, select a tree or a flagpole and have the students spread out and stand at such a distance from the object that its height subtends for them an angle of 20 degrees. See how closely the students are thus able to form a circle around the object.

Once students are able to estimate angles using their hands and arms, it is time to measure some astronomical angles. Inside the classroom, use the overhead projector to show the students the circumpolar constellations. Poke small holes in a manila folder to make a workable star chart for the overhead. Use figure 1-2 as a pattern. I used a thin, opaque sheet

# NORTHERN CIRCUMPOLAR STARS

Schedar ○

Caph ○

Gamma ○ ○ Ruchbah
Cassiopeiae

○ Epsilon
Cassiopeiae

CASSIOPEIA

Polaris ○
NCP ✝

URSA MAJOR

Dubhe ○

Alcor ○
Mizar ○ ○ Alioth ○ Megrez ○ Merak

Alkaid ○ ○ Phecda
(Benetnasch) (Phad)

Figure 1-2

18

of polystyrene plastic and drilled small holes whose areas were calculated to be proportional to the magnitudes of the individual stars. The students will need to learn how to recognize Ursa Major and Cassiopeia and to find Polaris.

Unless you teach night school, the next exercise will have to be a homework assignment. You might be able to schedule a star party for an evening at school so that all the students can work together. The students are to measure some or all of the following things:

- the altitude angle of Polaris (equal to your latitude)
- the separation angle of the stars Merak and Dubhe, the pointer stars of Ursa Major (just above 5 degrees)
- the separation of Alkaid and Dubhe, at opposite ends of Ursa Major (about 25 degrees)
- the separation of Polaris and Dubhe (about 30 degrees)
- the separation of Polaris and Alkaid (40 degrees)
- the separation angle of the stars Schedar and Caph, the two brightest stars in Cassiopeia (5 degrees)
- the separation of Caph and Epsilon Cassiopeiae, the stars at opposite ends of Cassiopeia (more than 15 degrees)
- the separation of Polaris and Caph (about 30 degrees)
- the separation of Polaris and Epsilon Cassiopeiae (just over 25 degrees)
- the angular diameter of the moon (about 1/2 degree)

The moon's angular size is best found when the moon is between first quarter and full. Be sure that students measure the widest extent of the moon if it is less than full.

# Cross Staff

The basic form of a cross staff is shown in figure 1-3. Remember that measuring angles with a cross staff—or any other instrument—will be meaningless for students unless they have first learned to estimate these angles.

To make the cross staff, each student will need a 3" x 5" card and a piece of string about one meter long. Begin by having the students cut out the pattern shown in figure 1-4. Use a sharp pencil to poke a small hole at the spot indicated by the "x". Tie a knot in one end of the string and thread the string through the hole until it is stopped by the knot. Next, tell the students to hold the cards at arm's length and draw circles on them of a size equal to what they think the full moon would look like.

The cross staff is used by looking at the target object(s) and moving the card until one opening just frames the target. Then mark and measure the distance from your eye to the card. Start by holding the string near the card mask and press the string against your cheek just under your eye. Now move the card away with the other hand, pulling the string between finger and cheek as it goes, until the target is just framed. Then hold the string at that point and measure the distance from there to the card.

To find the angle you have observed, you could measure the distance along the string (call it X) and the width of the opening in the card (call it Y). The angle can then be found from the following formula:

$$\text{Angle} = 2 \times \arctan (Y / (2 \times X))$$

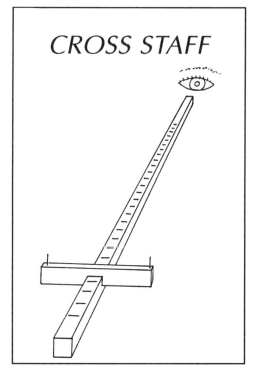

*CROSS STAFF*

Figure 1-3

# *CROSS STAFF PATTERN*

A = 1 cm

B = 5 cm

Cut away part of a 3" x 5" index card so that what remains looks like the pattern above. Using a sharp pencil, poke a tiny hole in the card at the "+" sign. Tie a large knot in one end of a 1 meter length of string and thread the string through the hole to complete your cross staff.

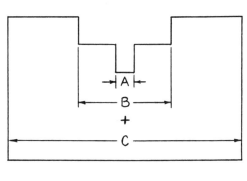

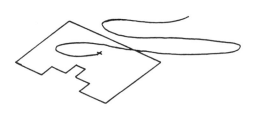

Figure 1-4

The chart labeled "Cross Staff Angles" (figure 1-5) can be used to convert the distance measurements into angles. Students have to note whether they used frame A (1 cm), frame B (5 cm), or mask C (12.7 cm, the whole length of the card).

Students are to use their cross staffs to measure the same astronomical angles they did with their hands. In class, compile students' data and find the class averages. Compare the values with accepted values to see which students made the best measurements. Also, see how accurately they sketched the moon on the cross staffs before observing. Most people greatly overestimate the moon's angular size.

# Angular Size of the Sun

Worksheet 1C, "Angular Size of the Sun" (page 26), will have to be done on a sunny day. Students should work in teams of two or three. Have them prop up the box they use so that it will not move at all while they make their observations.

After finishing the exercise you may want to have a discussion with the whole class in which the following questions are considered:

- How do the angular diameters of the sun and moon compare? (They are almost exactly the same.)

## CROSS STAFF ANGLES

| Distance | A (1 cm) | B (5 cm) | C (12.7 cm) |
|---|---|---|---|
| 57 cm | 1 degree | 5 degrees | |
| 56 | | | |
| 55 | | | |
| 54 | | | |
| 53 | | | |
| 52 | | | |
| 51 | | | |
| 50 | | | |
| 49 | | | |
| 48 | | 6 | 15 degrees |
| 47 | | | |
| 46 | | | |
| 45 | | | |
| 44 | | | |
| 43 | | | |
| 42 | | | |
| 41 | | 7 | |
| 40 | | | |
| 39 | | | |
| 38 | | | |
| 37 | | | |
| 36 | | 8 | 20 |
| 35 | | | |
| 34 | | | |
| 33 | | | |
| 32 | | 9 | |
| 31 | | | |
| 30 | | | |
| 29 | 2 | 10 | 25 |
| 28 | | | |
| 27 | | | |
| 26 | | 11 | |
| 25 | | | |
| 24 | | 12 | 30 |
| 23 | | | |
| 22 | | 13 | |
| 21 | | | |
| 20 | | 14 | 35 |
| 19 | 3 | 15 | |
| 18 | | 16 | |
| 17 | | 17 | 40 |
| 16 | | 18 | |
| 15 | | 19 | 45 |
| 14 | 4 | 20 | 50 |
| 13 | | | |
| 12 | | | 55 |
| 11 | 5 | 25 | 60 |

Figure 1-5

- Does this mean that the sun and moon are actually the same size? (Only if they are the same distance away. If not, then the more distant one is larger.)
- Can you tell whether the sun or the moon is nearer Earth? How can you tell? Hint: What is an eclipse? (During a solar eclipse, the moon passes between the sun and us, so the moon must be closer than the sun.)
- How do the distances of the sun and moon compare? (The sun is farther away from us than the moon is.)
- How must their sizes compare? (The sun must be larger than the moon.)

Students should have found that the angular diameters of the sun and the moon are about the same, about 1/2 degree. They should recognize that this does *not* mean that they are actually the same size. Even the ancients knew that the moon is the nearest celestial object because it eclipses all others, so we know that the sun is farther away than the moon. Since their angular sizes are the same, the sun must be larger. In fact, it can be shown that the ratio of their sizes must be the same as the ratio of their distances, so that if it turned out that the sun were 20 times as far away as the moon, then its actual diameter would be 20 times as large as the moon's.

Have students fill in the spaces labeled "moon's angular extent" and "sun's angular extent" on worksheet 1D, "Our Neighborhood in Space" (pages 29 and 30, respectively).

# Further Explorations

## Report

Research and prepare an oral report on one of the following instruments: astrolabe, cross staff, back staff, quadrant, octant, sextant. Tell when and by whom it was invented, what it was used for, and how it worked.

## Project

Build a model of one of the instruments listed above and demonstrate how it works.

# ANGLES, SIZE, AND DISTANCE
## Worksheet 1A

A

1. Use a ruler to measure the diameters of the three circles in the photo above. How do the diameters compare?

2. Are the three balls in the photo really the same size?

3. How do you explain the fact that they appear the same size in the photograph but are really not the same size at all?

B

C

4. Can you tell which balls are closest and which are farthest away from the camera in drawings B and C above?

5. Is your thumb bigger than your friend's head? Hold out your thumb at arm's length and line it up on another student's head. Have the other student walk away until his head is just covered up by your thumb. Obviously, his head did not really get smaller as he walked away; so what, exactly, did get smaller?

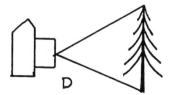

D

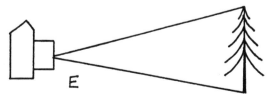

E

6. In which drawing, D or E, will the tree appear bigger? Why?

The size of an image you see depends on the angular extent of the image, measured from your eye. The size of an image on a photograph depends on the angular extent of the object photographed, measured from the camera.

The angle that the observer would measure from one end of the object to the other is the angle that the object *subtends* for the observer. In figure D the tree subtends angle X; in figure E it subtends angle Y.

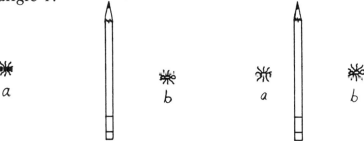

7.  In the above drawing, what angle does the pencil on the left subtend for ant a? For ant b? To which ant does the pencil look longer?

8.  In the drawing on the right, ant a has crawled closer to the pencil. What angle does the pencil subtend for it now?

9.  Here is another pencil. How far away from it would an ant have to be for the pencil to subtend an angle of 90 degrees?

10. What is the largest angle the pencil could subtend? Where would the ant have to be for this to happen?

11. What is the smallest angle the pencil could subtend? Where would the ant have to be for this to occur?

12. Figure H represents a photograph of a tree taken from a distance of 20 meters. Draw what the photo would look like if the same camera took a picture from 10 meters away. Now draw the result if the camera were 40 meters away. Be sure to label your drawings with the distances from camera to tree.

# BODY-MEASURED ANGLES
## Worksheet 1B

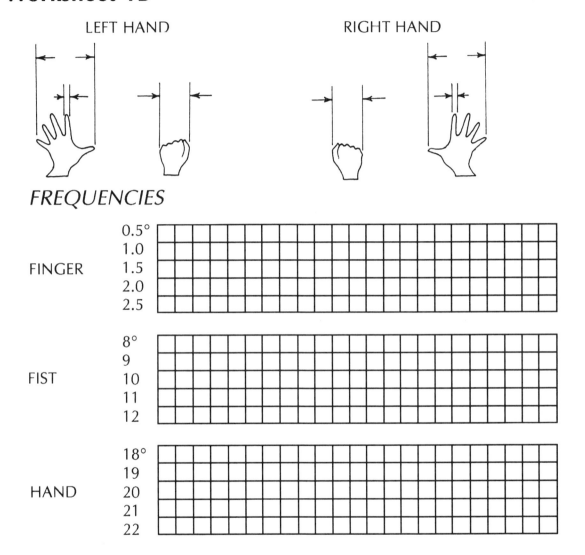

LEFT HAND       RIGHT HAND

*FREQUENCIES*

FINGER

| 0.5° |
| 1.0 |
| 1.5 |
| 2.0 |
| 2.5 |

FIST

| 8° |
| 9 |
| 10 |
| 11 |
| 12 |

HAND

| 18° |
| 19 |
| 20 |
| 21 |
| 22 |

## CLASS AVERAGES

|  | MEAN | MEDIAN | MODE |
|---|---|---|---|
| FINGER |  |  |  |
| FIST |  |  |  |
| HAND |  |  |  |

# ANGULAR SIZE OF THE SUN
## Worksheet 1C

**Materials:**

Large cardboard box
Small piece of aluminum foil
Plain white paper
Adding machine tape
Straight pin
Metric ruler
Tape

**Overview:**

Scientists believe that the sun is slowly expanding. Millions of years ago it was slightly smaller in volume than it is now.

1.  If you could have measured the angular size of the sun at the time of the dinosaurs, would it have subtended a larger or smaller angle than it does today? Assume that Earth has always been the same distance from the sun.

2.  To know what angle the sun will subtend in the future, we need to know its angular extent today. Could you measure this the same way you measured the moon's angular extent? Explain your answer.

3.  To measure the sun, you will project the sun's image onto a sheet of paper. **NEVER LOOK DIRECTLY AT THE SUN!** You will make your solar projector from the materials listed above. Draw a picture of what you think the device will look like.

**Procedure:**

1.  Make your solar projector.

    a.  Use your pencil to poke a hole in one end of the box.

    b.  Tape the foil in place over the hole.

    c.  In the center of the hole made by the pencil, use the pin to poke a tiny hole in the foil.

    d.  Place a sheet of paper flat against the inside of the box opposite the pinhole. Tape it in place.

2.  Set up your projector in the sun and gather your data.

    a.  Prop it up so the sun shines through the pinhole to form an image on the paper.

PI IN THE SKY © 1993 Zephyr Press, Tucson, AZ

  b. Trace around the image with a pencil and note the time.

  c. Watch the image for a few minutes. What happens? Why?

  d. When the image has just moved completely out of its former circle, note the time again and trace the image in its new position.

  e. What do you think would happen if you enlarged the hole? Enlarge the hole and describe what happens to the image.

  f. With the edge of another piece of paper cover one-half of the hole. What is the shape of the hole now? What happened to the sun's image? Can you explain it?

3.  Analyze your data.

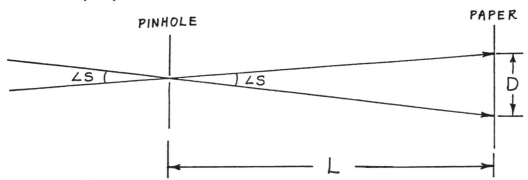

In the drawing above, the arrows represent rays of light coming from opposite sides of the sun. Angle S is the angle the sun subtends. You can find the measure of this angle from D, the diameter of the sun's image, and L, the distance from the pinhole to the paper in your box.

  a. Measure D and L in centimeters and record the results.

  b. On the adding machine tape, draw a line segment equal in length to L. At one end of this segment, at a right angle to it, draw another line of length D. Finally, draw a third line to complete a triangle. Measure angle S and estimate the error in your result.

  c. How long does it take for the sun to appear to travel all the way around Earth (360 degrees)?

  d. How long did it take your image to move one image diameter? What fraction of a whole day is this?

  e. What fraction of 360 is the sun's angular extent? How many degrees is that?

  f. How does your answer to 3e compare with that to 3b?

# OUR NEIGHBORHOOD IN SPACE: EARTH

## Worksheet 1D

| QUANTITY | OUR RESULT | ACCEPTED VALUE | REASONS FOR ERROR | WAYS TO IMPROVE |
|---|---|---|---|---|
| EARTH'S CIRCUMFERENCE | | | | |
| EARTH'S DIAMETER | | | | |
| ALTITUDE ANGLE OF POLARIS | | | | |
| OUR LATITUDE | | | | |
| OUR LONGITUDE | | | | |
| OBLIQUITY (TILT OF EARTH'S AXIS) | | | | |

OUR NEIGHBORHOOD IN SPACE: MOON

| QUANTITY | OUR RESULT | ACCEPTED VALUE | REASONS FOR ERROR | WAYS TO IMPROVE |
|---|---|---|---|---|
| MOON'S ANGULAR EXTENT | | | | |
| MOON'S DIAMETER/ EARTH'S UMBRA DIAMETER AT MOON'S DISTANCE | | | | |
| MOON'S DISTANCE | | | | |
| MOON'S DIAMETER | | | | |
| MOON'S ANGULAR VELOCITY | | | | |
| MOON'S SYNODIC PERIOD | | | | |

# OUR NEIGHBORHOOD IN SPACE: SUN

| QUANTITY | OUR RESULT | ACCEPTED VALUE | REASONS FOR ERROR | WAYS TO IMPROVE |
|---|---|---|---|---|
| SUN'S ANGULAR EXTENT | | | | |
| ANGLE BETWEEN SUN AND MOON AT QUARTER PHASE | | | | |
| HOW MANY TIMES FURTHER AWAY THE SUN IS THAN THE MOON | | | | |
| SUN'S DISTANCE | | | | |
| SUN'S DIAMETER | | | | |
| DISTANCE TO NEAREST STARS | | | | |

# CHAPTER 2
## The Size of Earth

This chapter shows your students how to build a sun compass to find true north and, in cooperation with one or more distant colleagues, to compute the circumference of Earth.

## Background

Students of all ages will readily tell you that Earth is round, but few indeed can justify the assertion with more than an appeal to the authority of a textbook. Can you? Without taking the word of a scientist or an author, could you prove to a doubter that Earth is shaped like a ball?

Because it is so large compared with most of our units of measure, Earth is not obviously round. We must look for subtle effects. If you watch with binoculars or a telescope as a ship sails out to sea, its hull will vanish first (see figure 2-1). Assuming that you didn't just witness a sinking, we may conclude that Earth is not flat.

While you're at the seashore, carefully measure the angle from zenith to horizon. It should turn out to be almost exactly 90 degrees. Now hike to the top of a very tall mountain and try the same thing. This time the angle should turn out to be very slightly greater than 90 degrees.

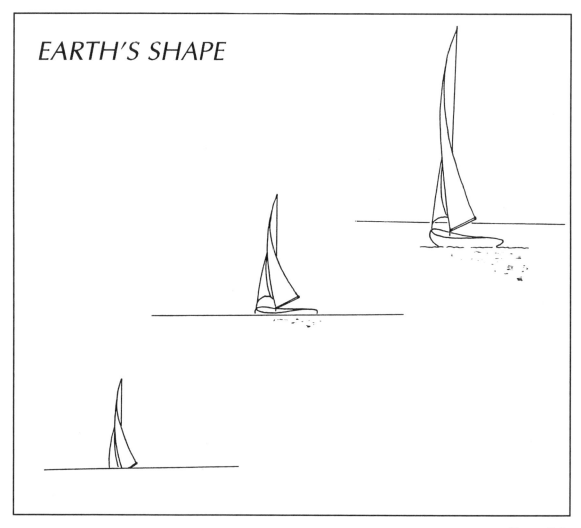

EARTH'S SHAPE

Figure 2-1

By now it should be dark, so look for Polaris, the North Star, and measure the angle from it to the horizon. Note that this angle remains nearly constant for any given place on Earth from which the star is visible. Travel north and discover that the angle increases as you go. This could be because either the star is very far away and Earth is round or the star is close to a flat Earth. To find out which is the case, travel south. If Earth is flat, as you travel the star will appear to approach—but never quite touch—the horizon. If Earth is round, as you travel the star will approach the horizon at a uniform rate and finally disappear below it (see figures 2-2 and 2-3).

My favorite demonstration requires the least effort of all. Wait until the next lunar eclipse and observe it. No binoculars or telescopes are needed. The full moon will become dark as the moon passes through the shadow of Earth. The edge of Earth's shadow, as it passes across the face of the moon, is clearly curved!

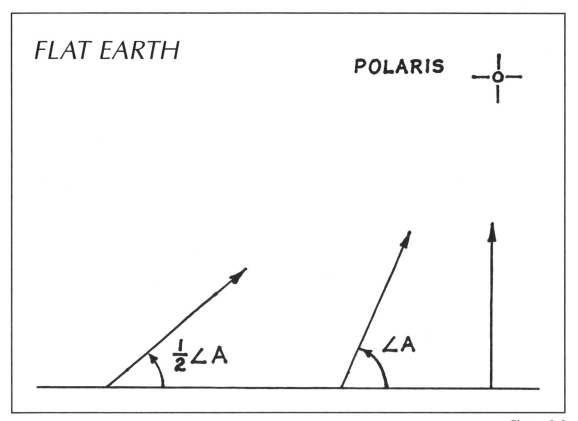

Figure 2-2

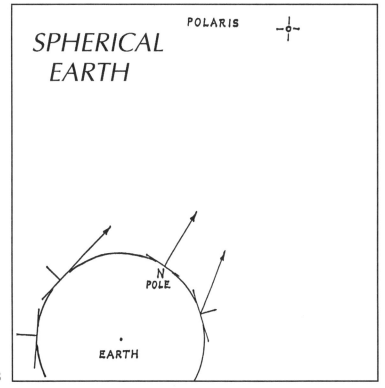

Figure 2-3

33

Thousands of years ago these effects were observed and some thinkers correctly interpreted them as evidence that Earth is a ball. In fact, from the time of Plato (ca. 350 B.C.) the spherical shape of Earth was seldom disputed by philosophers.

More than this, about 2,200 years ago Earth's size was computed with astonishing accuracy. The feat was accomplished by Eratosthenes of Cyrene (ca. 276–195 B.C.), the very one who gave us the famous sieve for finding prime numbers. After being educated in Athens, Eratosthenes was called, around 245 B.C., by Ptolemy III of Egypt to take charge of the fabled library at Alexandria, one of the world's greatest centers of learning.

Eratosthenes knew that Earth is spherical and devised an inventive way to compute its size. Near the southern border of Egypt lay the town of Syene, now called Aswan. It was known that in Syene, on the day of the summer solstice, the sun would pass through the zenith. At that moment a vertical style (gnomon) would cast no shadow and the sun would shine straight down into a vertical well.

Syene was very near the first cataract of the Nile; Alexandria was near the Nile's mouth, some 500 miles almost due north. In Alexandria on the day of the summer solstice the sun did not reach the zenith. Eratosthenes knew that the difference in the sun's zenith angles was due to the curvature of Earth between the latitudes of Syene and Alexandria.

Eratosthenes set up a gnomon at Alexandria and used it to measure the sun's zenith angle as the sun crossed the meridian on the day of the summer solstice. He knew the distance from Syene to Alexandria; he used this and the angle he observed to compute Earth's circumference.

In the figure called "Eratosthenes" (figure 2-4) you see Earth in cross section. Two locations on its surface, which have the same longitude but different latitudes, are marked by the two gnomons. Eratosthenes made the correct critical assumption that the sun is so far from Earth that the sun's rays are essentially parallel at the two locations. Angle A is the zenith angle of the sun as it crosses the meridian of the southern location; angle B is the zenith angle at the northern location. Angle C is the angle between the two locations measured from the center of Earth; it is the difference of the two locations' latitudes.

The figure also explains the simple relationship among angles A, B, and C. The three angles of the triangle measure A, C, and 180-B, where the angles are given in degrees. Since their sum must be 180 degrees (for any plane triangle the interior angles sum to 180 degrees), we can derive the relation:

$$C = B - A$$

In Eratosthenes' case this was especially simple, since A = 0, but in our replication of his experiment we will need the more general relation.

Knowing angle A, angle B, and d, the distance between the two locations, finding Earth's circumference simply means solving the following proportion:

$$C / 360 = d / \text{circumference}$$

The angle Eratosthenes measured for the zenith angle at Alexandria was one-fiftieth of a full circle, or about 7.2 degrees. Using Eratosthenes' measurement and the fact that Syene and Alexandria were about 500 miles apart, calculate Earth's circumference. Compare your answer to the accepted value for the polar circumference, 24,820 miles.

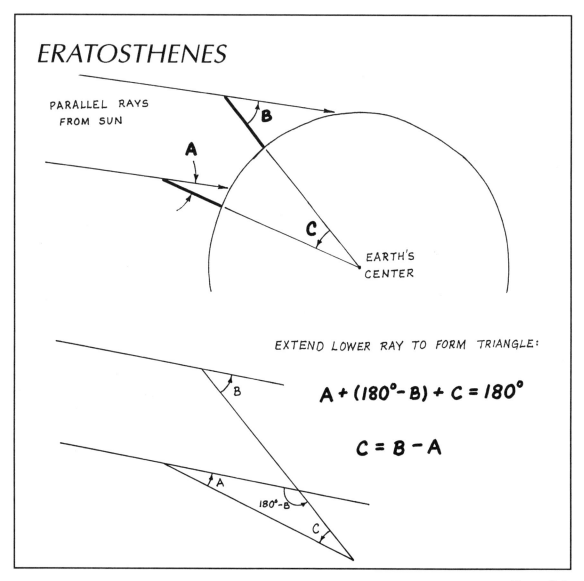

Figure 2-4

In order to duplicate Eratosthenes' experiment, you will need the cooperation of a colleague at a location several hundred miles north or south of yours. Each of you will set up a gnomon and use it to measure the zenith angle of the sun as it crosses your meridian on an agreed-upon day.

Choosing another location is easier than it might appear. Ideally, the two places should have the same longitude—one is directly north of the other. In this case the sun crosses the meridian of both locations at the same time. If the longitudes are different, the sun will cross the meridian of the eastern location first.

In the time between the two meridian transits the sun's declination will change and some of the difference in zenith angle will be attributable to this effect.

In reality, though, the sun's declination changes so slowly that your results will not be appreciably affected even if the two locations have widely differing longitudes. Near the times of the equinoxes, for example, when the sun's declination changes most rapidly, it moves less than 1/60 degree per hour. Since our crude apparatus will give results accurate only to perhaps 1/4 degree, the two locations could safely be as far as eight hours or 120 degrees apart.

An important consideration is that the distance, d, that you will need is the north-south component of the distance between the two locations. Clearly, only if the two locations have nearly the same longitude will the distance between them be a good approximation to d (see figure 2-5).

# Preparation

## Materials

Pine boards, about one foot square and one inch thick, each with a 1/4-inch diameter hole drilled normal (perpendicular) to the flat surface and located near one edge
One or more circular bubble levels
Ice cream sticks
Plain white paper
Pencils
Chalk
Masking tape
World globe
Darts with suction cup tips
Large rubber bands

Light bulb and socket
String
Inflatable world globes or volleyballs
Conference telephone or postcards

To work well, the gnomon should be precisely normal (perpendicular) to the base—the pine board. Use a drill press to make the holes; perhaps the shop teacher at your school can do this for you. You may find that a hole 17/64" in diameter works perfectly when standard pencils are used as gnomons.

If you are acquainted with someone who lives several hundred miles north or south of you and who is willing to perform this experiment with you, agree on the dates for the exercise and send him or her a letter explaining the procedure. It is best to select several dates, as the weather may cause problems at one or both locations.

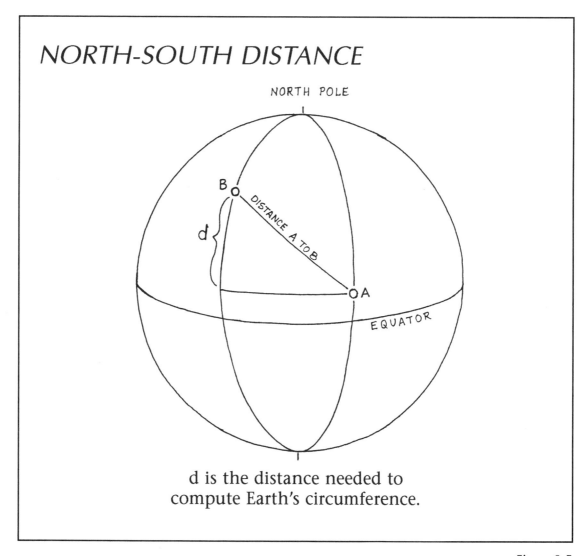

## NORTH-SOUTH DISTANCE

d is the distance needed to
compute Earth's circumference.

Figure 2-5

If you don't know anyone who is willing to help you, just look at a map and choose some communities at least 500 miles north or south of you. Use telephone books in your local public library to look up the names, addresses, and telephone numbers of some schools in those communities. Call the principals of those schools, describe your project, and ask to speak to a science or math teacher who is likely to be interested in participating in such a project. Talk to this teacher and pique his or her interest before sending the letter explaining the procedure. I have found that it is best, when dealing with such people, to include a stamped, self-addressed envelope with every piece of correspondence to maximize the likelihood of getting a reply.

After you have made these arrangements you will need to find the north-south distance between the two locations. In principle, the distance could be paced off by walking due north or south to the latitude of the other location. In practice, I cheat. The necessary distance can easily be computed from the latitudes of the two locations by using a tabulated value for the polar circumference of Earth. Of course, the final results we obtain are based on circular reasoning, but you need not reveal the source of your figures. My inspiration here was a college professor who claimed he would lie, cheat, steal, and in fact do anything but murder to get his students to learn. Clearly, in theory the distance could be found without resorting to prior knowledge of Earth's size (and to date no student of mine has questioned the source of the data).

## Build Sun Compasses

Have the student teams construct their compasses by fitting sharpened pencils into the boards, eraser ends first. Make sure the pencils fit tightly into the holes—wrap the pencils with tape if necessary. Also make sure each pencil is perpendicular to the surface of the board. Students can check this with the corner of a sheet of paper. Finally, tape a blank sheet of paper onto the board.

Go outside and place each compass in the sun so that the gnomon's (pencil's) shadow falls on the paper. Carefully mark the tip of the shadow on the paper with another pencil. Before returning to the classroom, push the second pencil into the ground point first and orient it so that it casts no shadow. Leave the compasses and pencils in position while everyone goes inside.

Back inside, discuss what will happen to the shadow on the compass. Will it change direction? Length? Both? In what way? Will it get longer or shorter? Will it move clockwise or counterclockwise around the gnomon?

How long must you wait to see a measurable change? What will it look like in 10 minutes?

The shadow on the compass will almost always change in direction and length. In the morning, before local apparent noon, the shadow shortens; after the sun crosses your meridian it lengthens. Whether the shadow will move clockwise or counterclockwise around the gnomon depends on your latitude and the time of the year. If the sun's declination is less than your latitude, then it will move clockwise; otherwise the motion is counterclockwise. If you live above latitude 23.5 degrees north, then the motion is always clockwise. You need to wait only a few minutes to see a noticeable change in the shadow.

Also discuss how to find north. A Boy Scout trick is to place a stick into the ground so that no shadow is cast. A little while later, when the shadow appears, it points very roughly in one of the four cardinal directions. Which one? (East.) Why? (Because the sun moves east to west across the sky.)

Now go back outside and mark the new shadow's tip on the paper and observe the shadow now cast by the second pencil. Which direction is north? Which direction did the shadow move and how does this relate to the sun's apparent motion in the sky? The students should discover that the length of the shadow tells you the sun's altitude angle. You may explain that the direction of the shadow tells you the sun's azimuth angle, an angle that is normally measured clockwise from north.

Each team needs to select a spot on cement or asphalt where it will set up the compass for the rest of the experiments. First we will find north precisely, now that we have it approximately. Orient the compass with the gnomon on the south side of the board. Once it is in place, trace around the board with chalk and write the team members' initials on the cement inside the tracing. With the compass in position, make it perfectly level by shimming it up with ice cream sticks and tape while checking it with the circular bubble level. Tape a clean sheet of paper on the compass and then store it until tomorrow. Be sure to leave the pencil gnomon in place from now until the end of the experiment.

## Finding True North

To use the sun compasses, students will need to mark the tip of the gnomon's shadow several times during a day, both before and after local apparent noon. Doing it after each class period works well, as each observation takes only a few minutes and the students really enjoy having an excuse to arrive late to their classes. If students can't leave their compasses

in place all day, they will have to store them in your classroom and take them out to their designated spots just for the observations, being careful each time to put the compasses in precisely the same locations and orientations. Before removing the pencil gnomon at the end of the day, have the students measure its height with a metric ruler and record the result on the paper.

In class, discuss how we know Earth is round. Then hand out worksheet 2A, "Earth and Sun" (page 47), and have students answer the questions on it after observing your demonstration. Use the globe to demonstrate how the curvature of Earth can be seen by watching a boat disappear hull first as it sails away.

Turn on the light bulb to represent the sun and turn off the room lights. Demonstrate the way Earth rotates and revolves about the sun as you pose the questions on the worksheet. Place a rubber suction cup dart on the globe to represent a gnomon somewhere on the surface of Earth and continue rotating and revolving as you pose questions 13 through 20 (pages 47–48).

Turn the room lights back on and have student teams make their own globes using the inflatable plastic globes or volleyballs. First, add a rubber band to represent the equator. Then, find the poles and mark them with tape. Place a suction cup dart at the latitude of your location. This the students may approximate by what "looks right" or they may find it accurately by measuring the distance from equator to pole with the string and a metric ruler and then solving the following proportion:

latitude / 90 degrees  =  X / distance from equator to pole

On pieces of tape at your city's location draw the directions north, south, east, and west.

Have students demonstrate their knowledge by using their globes to do the following:

- Show how Earth spins on its axis. Show how far it turns in 3 hours, 6 hours, 12 hours, and so on.
- With the light bulb/sun on, show how Earth is oriented when it is noon at your city. Also show sunrise, sunset, and midnight.
- Tell what direction the gnomon's shadow points at sunrise (roughly west), noon (north or south), and sunset (roughly east).
- Tell at what times the shadow is shortest and longest (shortest at local apparent noon, longest at sunrise or sunset).
- Imagine another dart at the north pole, where it would point to Polaris. If you lived at the north pole, tell where in the sky you would look to see Polaris (straight up).

- Living where you do, tell where in the sky you find Polaris (look north at an altitude angle equal to your latitude).
- Tell where you would look for Polaris if you lived at the equator (look north on the horizon).

Tell where on Earth you would be if you found Polaris a given number of degrees above the horizon (on a circle of latitude equal to this same number of degrees).

## Finding Your Meridian

Any day after the shadow path has been traced on the sun compass you can find your meridian. The points of the shadow's tip should fall on a smooth curve (see figure 2-6). A line through the gnomon and the shadow when the shadow was shortest defines the meridian, that is, points north. To find this line, students will need compasses and straightedges. First, measure the height of the gnomon, if that has not already been done. Then, remove the pencil gnomon from the compass, but leave the paper taped in place.

The procedure for finding the meridian is illustrated in figure 2-7. Draw a smooth curve through the points. Using the gnomon's location as a center, draw an arc that crosses the smooth curve at two points. Construct the line through these two points. Neglecting the very small effect of the changing declination of the sun during the few hours around noon, this line runs true east-west. Construct the perpendicular bisector of this line segment and verify that it passes through the gnomon. This bisector runs north-south; it is the meridian. The students should mark the north and south edges of the paper where this line crosses it.

Now find the altitude and zenith angles of the sun at local apparent noon (see figure 2-8). To do this, measure the distance from

SUN COMPASS 1

⊙ GNOMON

Figure 2-6

41

## USING A SUN COMPASS

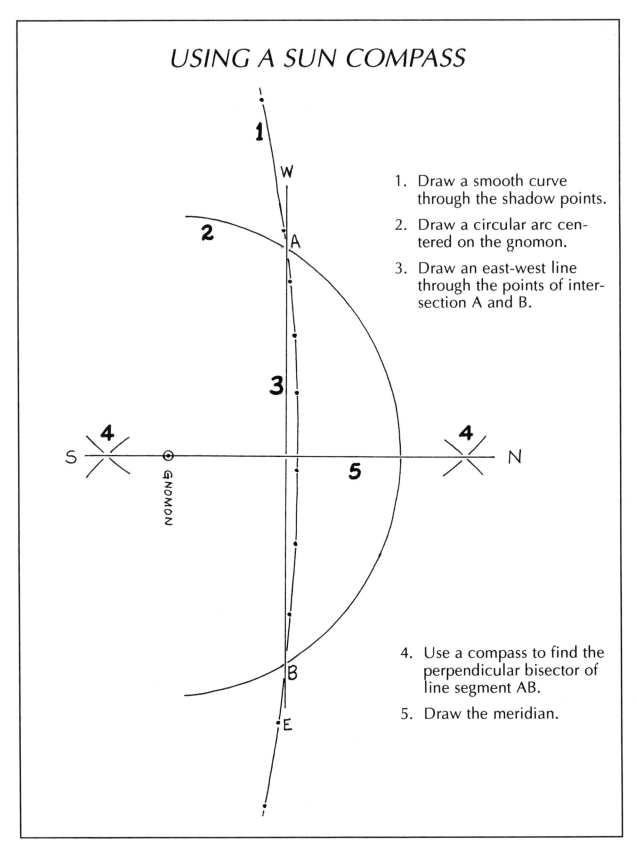

1.  Draw a smooth curve through the shadow points.

2.  Draw a circular arc centered on the gnomon.

3.  Draw an east-west line through the points of intersection A and B.

4.  Use a compass to find the perpendicular bisector of line segment AB.

5.  Draw the meridian.

Figure 2-7

gnomon to shadow curve along the meridian. On a blank sheet of paper mark the gnomon's height and the shadow's length along two adjacent sides, measured from the same corner. Complete the right triangle by drawing in the hypotenuse and measure the sun's altitude and zenith angles with a protractor.

This is a good time to discuss Eratosthenes' method for finding the circumference of Earth. Ask students what altitude and zenith angles they would expect to find on the same day from a city north or south of yours.

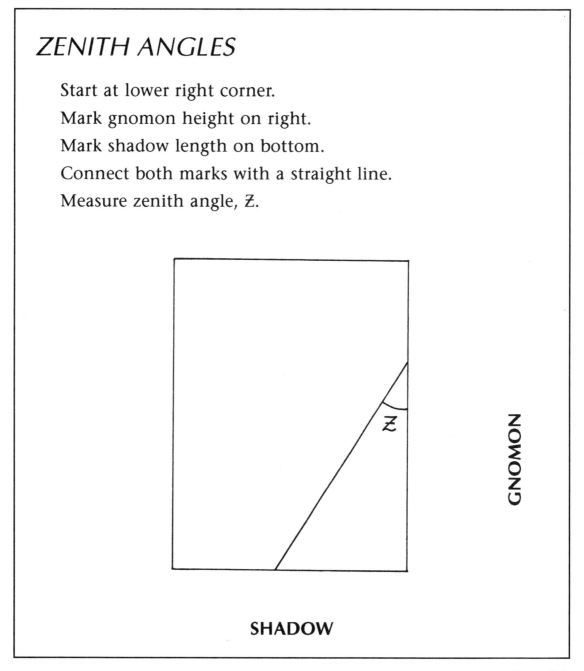

## ZENITH ANGLES

Start at lower right corner.

Mark gnomon height on right.

Mark shadow length on bottom.

Connect both marks with a straight line.

Measure zenith angle, Z̄.

Figure 2-8

# Earth's Circumference

This is the payoff for all your work. Exchange the data you have found with your colleagues in other parts of the world. The best method is by telephone, using a conference phone if available so that all the students can hear what is said. If this isn't possible, an exchange of letters or post-cards will suffice. You need to exchange the values found for the sun's zenith angle and the north-south distance between your two locales. Additionally, you may exchange altitude angles for Polaris.

Finally you get to compute Earth's circumference. Call the north-south distance between the observation points D and the difference between your two zenith angles Z, measured in degrees. To find the circumference you need only solve this proportion:

$$\text{Circumference} / D = 360 / Z$$

Compare your results with the value tabulated in books. Ask students what they could do to improve their outcomes.

Be sure to have the students record their results on worksheet 1D, "Our Neighborhood in Space" (pages 28–30). Fill in Earth's circumference, Earth's diameter, Polaris's altitude angle, and your latitude.

# Further Explorations

## Problem 1

Someone standing on top of a mountain 3 miles high measured the angle from his nadir to his horizon and found it to be 87.8 degrees. Use this to find the radius of Earth in miles.

## Problem 2

A certain ship measures 10 feet from water line to deck. Lying on the beach near the water you watch it sail out of sight, using binoculars as necessary. How far away will it be when the hull just disappears?

## Problem 3

If you could walk around Earth along a great circle, how long would it take you?

## Problem 4

Each day, the sun rises in the east and sets in the west. If you could travel east to west fast enough, the sun would appear to you not to move across the sky; you could keep up with the sun. If an airliner could keep up with the sun, a passenger could leave New York at 6:00 A.M. and arrive in San Francisco at 6:00 A.M. (San Francisco time) the same day.

   a. Is there any place on Earth where you could keep up with the sun by walking?
   b. How fast would an airplane have to fly along the equator to keep up with the sun? (You may neglect the effect of the plane's altitude.)
   c. What if you take the plane's altitude into account, and it is flying at 10,000 feet?
   d. Where on Earth could an airplane keep up with the sun by flying 600 miles per hour?
   e. How fast would the plane have to go to make the trip from New York to San Francisco mentioned above?

## Puzzle 1

Imagine a measuring tape stretched tightly all the way around Earth. If the tape is lengthened by one foot and adjusted to be everywhere the same distance away from Earth's surface, how far away from the surface will it be?

## Puzzle 2

Last summer a man went camping. One morning he had some coffee, broke camp, and began to hike. He walked due south at 4 miles per hour for 15 minutes and then turned east and strode at the same speed for 30 minutes. At this point he realized that he had left his coffee pot, still half full of coffee, back at his campsite. He turned 270 degrees and was able to hike straight back. He found his campsite and his coffee pot apparently undisturbed; but when he upturned the pot, not a drop came out.

   a. What happened to the coffee?
   b. Where was his campsite located?
   c. Where else on Earth could his campsite have been?

## Puzzle 3

A man at the airport in Perth, Australia, was very upset because he had just missed his plane. An attractive woman offered to help him. She explained that she owned her own private jet and was about to leave on a trip herself. Even though she didn't yet know where he wanted to go, she would be glad to take him there. He demurred at first, saying he was afraid it would be very inconvenient for her, but finally accepted after she explained that wherever he went would not be out of her way.

- Where was she going?
- Where else on Earth could this incident have taken place?

## Report

Research and present an oral report on Eratosthenes. Find out, if possible, what kind of person he was and list his accomplishments. Describe the library of Alexandria, of which he was in charge. What happened to it and its contents?

## Project

Given a world globe, find its diameter by estimating with a meterstick and then by measuring its circumference with a piece of string.

Compute the scale to which the globe is made. Use an encyclopedia to find the appropriate information so that you can compute how high the mountains would be and how deep the oceans would be if they were shrunk to this scale.

# EARTH AND SUN
## Worksheet 2A

1. How do you know Earth is round? How would you prove it to someone who didn't believe it?

Observe the models of Earth and the sun demonstrated by the teacher and then answer the following questions:

2. What is the terminator?

3. How much of Earth is lighted at one time?

4. Where on Earth is it day? Where is it night?

5. Where on the globe is it sunrise? Where is it sunset?

6. Looking down on the north pole, does Earth rotate (spin) clockwise or counterclockwise?

7. Which direction is east? How do you know?

8. How far does Earth turn in 24 hours? 12? 6?

9. About how many hours is it from sunrise to sunset?

10. How many degrees per hour does Earth turn?

11. Looking down on the north pole, does Earth revolve (orbit) clockwise or counterclockwise around the sun?

12. How long does it take Earth to revolve around the sun?

Use a suction cup dart on the globe to represent a vertical pole on Earth's surface and then answer the following:

13. What is the subsolar point?

14. What time is it at that spot? Where else on Earth is it the same time?

15. Which direction does the shadow point at noon (if you live north of 23.5 degrees north latitude)?

16. How can you tell when it is noon by the shadow's length?

17. How can you find true north by using the shadow?

18. What direction does the shadow travel across Earth?

19. What direction does the sun travel across the sky?

20. Draw Earth and the sun in space, as seen from above the north pole. Show how Earth rotates and revolves.

# CHAPTER 3

# The Moon's Size and Distance from Earth

In this chapter you will use the moon's angular diameter found in chapter 1, the size of Earth computed in chapter 2, and a photograph of a lunar eclipse to calculate the moon's size and its distance from Earth.

## Background

We saw in the last chapter that Eratosthenes found the true circumference of the world some 1,700 years before Columbus foolishly attempted his passage to the Indies. Had the Italian navigator known the full extent of his intended voyage—about 12,000 miles at best—he would certainly have reconsidered.

Napoleon claimed that the only true conquests are those gained by knowledge over ignorance. But knowledge is not eternal. Once the repository of three-quarters of a million scrolls, Eratosthenes' great library was burned and looted until only a tiny fraction of the ancient literature remained. Much of the work of the ancients is forever lost to us; we may never know the full extent of their accomplishments. The few scrolls not destroyed were scattered far and lay nearly forgotten for a thousand years. The rationale of book burners everywhere is revealed in a story of the Muslim caliph who ordered the destruction of the last remaining rolls at Alexandria: he reasoned that if the writings agreed with the holy Koran they were superfluous, whereas if they disagreed with it they were pernicious, so in any case it was best to destroy them.

Eratosthenes was one of many scholars to advance astronomy, only to be ignored for millennia. Even earlier, Aristarchus of Samos (fl. 281 B.C.) proposed a heliocentric universe some 1,700 years before Copernicus. Aristarchus also considered the problem of the sizes of and distances to the sun and moon and developed a method to calculate them using the peculiar geometric relationships that arise during solar and lunar eclipses. Aristarchus created his method as an exercise in mathematics and never (as far as we know from existent writings) actually computed the size of the moon. It remained for Hipparchus of Nicaea (second century B.C.) to do after he had refined Aristarchus' procedure.

An eclipse of the moon takes place when the moon, in its orbit around Earth (actually around the center of gravity of the Earth-moon system, located inside Earth), passes through Earth's shadow cast by the sun. During a lunar eclipse the three bodies are lined up in this order: sun, Earth, moon. Since the moon travels around Earth about once per month, you may wonder why lunar eclipses don't happen more often. The reason is that the plane of the moon's orbit is tilted with respect to the plane of Earth's orbit about the sun. Most of the time, therefore, the moon passes above or below the shadow of the Earth.

A lunar eclipse is an excellent demonstration of the shape of Earth. Using a photograph of the moon as it enters Earth's shadow, you will be able not only to see that the shadow is curved but to compare the shadow's radius to the size of the moon.

The moon's angular diameter measured from Earth determines a relationship between the moon's actual size and its distance from Earth. If you draw the angle (about one-half degree) on a large piece of paper you can see the possible sizes and distances; that is, the moon could be small and close by or it could be large and far away (see figure 3-1, top). If we find either the size or the distance from other information, we will be able to find the other quantity from this relationship.

By a significant coincidence, the angular diameter of the sun as measured from Earth is almost identical to that of the moon. You can verify this during a solar eclipse as the moon almost exactly covers the sun's face.

Since the sun is larger than Earth, Earth's shadow in space, called its *umbra*, is in the shape of a cone pointing away from the sun. Because the sun is so very far away compared to the size of Earth, the angle formed at the vertex of this cone is nearly equal to the sun's angular extent that we measure from Earth's surface. See the argument on page 97. Using the photograph of a lunar eclipse we will find the ratio of the moon's actual size to the diameter of the umbra. This will place the moon's size and distance in a new relationship (see figure 3-1, bottom).

# LUNAR REASONING

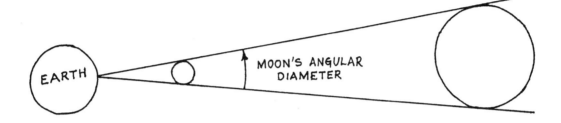

Possible sizes and locations of the moon
determined by the angular diameter.

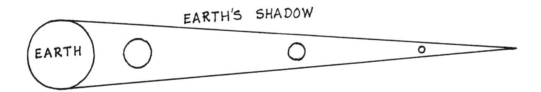

Possible sizes and locations of the moon
determined by the ratio of the
moon's size to the size of Earth's shadow.

Figure 3-1

You will draw two angles on a long sheet of paper, one representing the moon's angular extent, the other representing the size of the moon compared to Earth's umbra. Where the rays of the angles intersect on the paper is the location of the moon, with both its size and distance to the correct scale.

# Preparation

## Materials

Plain white paper, 8 1/2" x 11" or larger
Adding machine tape
Scissors
Compasses
Rulers
Metersticks
Light bulb and socket
Small foam plastic balls, 5 to 10 cm in diameter
Very long straightedges, such as 8-foot lengths of 1" x 2" pine
 or fir (optional)

## Relative Size and Distance

Worksheet 3A, "Angular Diameter" (page 59), shows students how to find the ratio of the moon's distance from Earth to its size. The moon's angular diameter, found in chapter 1, determines an envelope of possible values for the moon's size and distance. Just from its angular extent we can't tell whether the moon is small and nearby or large and far away, but we can find a definite ratio of distance to size. Then, if we can discover either its distance or its size by another means, we can use this ratio to find the other quantity. This strategy will be used again to find the size of the sun in chapter 4.

## The Moon's Phases

To understand what happens during a lunar eclipse, students need to know how the moon orbits Earth. They have certainly noticed the phases of the moon, but many students do not know why they occur. An excellent way to learn about the motions of Earth, the moon, and the sun is to model them.

Set up the light bulb in the center of the classroom, form the students into a circle around this "sun," and darken the rest of the room. This time the students' own heads will represent Earth, and their noses can represent your city. Begin by asking them to stand so it is noon in your city; then have them demonstrate midnight, sunrise, and sunset. Be sure they rotate in the proper direction (counterclockwise, if you live in the northern hemisphere) and ask them which way they should revolve around the sun (also counterclockwise).

Next, give each of the students a foam plastic ball to represent the moon. They should mount the balls on the ends of pencils and then hold their "moons" so as to see a crescent to the left of the sun. Set the moon in motion about Earth—counterclockwise again—and do the following:

- Observe the waxing crescent, first quarter, and waxing gibbous (Latin for "humpbacked") phases of the moon.
- Have the moon pass above Earth's shadow and observe the full moon.
- Continue the orbit and see the waning gibbous, last quarter, and waning crescent phases. Identify the moon's limb and its terminator.
- Have the moon pass below the sun and observe the new moon.

Continue into a second orbit and stop at the first quarter phase. Ask questions like the following:

- What is the angular separation of sun and moon? (About 90 degrees)
- On a day when the moon is at first quarter, does the moon come up before or after the sun? (After the sun, by about 6 hours)
- What time of day would the moon come up? (Noon)
- Can you see the moon during the daylight hours? (Yes, but some students won't believe you until you show them.)
- What time of day would the moon set? (About 6 hours after sunset, around midnight)

Have the moon continue to revolve another 90 degrees. This time it should enter Earth's shadow, causing a lunar eclipse. Ask questions like these:

- What shape is the edge of the shadow? (Curved)
- Which side of the moon darkens first? (Left or east)
- During what phase does a lunar eclipse occur? (Full moon)
- What time does the moon rise and set? (It rises about sunset and sets about sunrise)
- How many people on Earth would get to view the eclipse? (All those for whom it is night when the eclipse occurs)

Continue the moon's orbit until new moon. This time the moon should pass in front of the sun, causing a solar eclipse. Ask questions such as these:

- During what phase does a solar eclipse occur? (New moon)
- What time does the moon rise and set? (With the sun)
- Look at the shadows of the "moons" on the faces of the other students. How many people on Earth get to view a solar eclipse? (Only those few who happen to be on the small part of the Earth's surface that is in the moon's shadow)

Conclude with some general questions about the moon:

- Does the moon rotate? (Yes, with the same period as it revolves)
- Could you see sunrise on the moon? (Yes)
- How long is a day on the moon? (About 29 1/2 Earth days)
- Could you see Earthrise on the moon? (No; it keeps the same orientation toward Earth.)
- What would a lunar eclipse look like from the moon? (You would have to be on the side of the moon we see from Earth. It would be day for you and the Earth would pass in front of the sun. You would be facing the dark side of Earth, a large disk whose diameter would appear about four times as large as a full moon seen from Earth.)

## Earth's Shadow in Space

Worksheet 3B, "Earth's Shadow in Space" (pages 60–61), has the students discover the shape of Earth's umbra so that they will understand how we can use a lunar eclipse to help find the moon's actual size and distance.

### The Size of Earth's Umbra

The photograph of the lunar eclipse (figure 3-2) shows the moon when it has partially entered Earth's umbra, or shadow cone. We want to compare the size of the moon to the diameter of this cone at the moon's distance. Each student team needs a copy of the photo, paper, compass, scissors, and a ruler.

Have the students cut out circles from the paper in an attempt to match the curvatures of the moon's image and the shadow on the moon. They should not measure anything but should simply pick compass settings that look right to them. Each team should try several times.

When all teams have disks that seem right to them, have them measure the diameters of their disks and compute the ratio of moon diameter to shadow diameter. Find the class average of this ratio. In subsequent work the teams may use either their own values or the class average.

Figure 3-2

Advanced students can discover a way to use the Pythagorean Theorem to compute the diameters from measurements of the photo. Then they can use worksheet 3C, "Lunar Eclipse" (page 62), to follow this procedure and compare their results with what they found above.

You can now find a rough approximation to the size of the moon by assuming that Earth's umbra is not a cone but a cylinder extending into space. Using the ratio of moon diameter to umbra diameter and the size of Earth found earlier, estimate the size of the moon. Since the umbra is really a cone, will the actual size be larger or smaller than your estimate? (Smaller)

# Earth and the Moon to Scale

The graphical method of finding the moon's size and distance takes a large amount of space, since the angles we use are so small, and may require the students to work on the floor. Advanced students may use an alternative method outlined on worksheet 3D, "The Moon's Size and Distance" (pages 63–64).

Each team of students needs a piece of adding machine tape between 2 and 3 meters long, a ruler, a meterstick, and, optionally, a very long straightedge. The directions for the activity are given on worksheet 3E, "The Moon's Size and Distance 2" (pages 65–66).

Because of the tiny angles involved, students will have to work very carefully to get good results. Instead of laying out the umbra's vertex angle of 1/2 degree with a protractor—a task that is essentially impossible—use the fact that the tangent of this angle is about 0.009 to draw a triangle containing the angle. Figure 3-3 outlines the process. The entire drawing will be about 2 meters long, but all the action takes place in the half farthest from the vertex, so it can be done without the very long straightedge.

Because the angles are small, it will be difficult to tell exactly where the rays cross. Have each team make its best estimate of this location and then draw in the moon. It will automatically turn out to have the correct scale size and distance from the circle representing Earth.

Compile the results from all of the student teams and compute a class average. Compare this with accepted values of the moon's actual size and distance from Earth.

# Further Explorations

## Problem 1

- If you could do so, how long would it take you to walk to the moon?
- How long would it take you to drive there at an average speed of 50 mph?
- How long to fly at 2,000 mph?

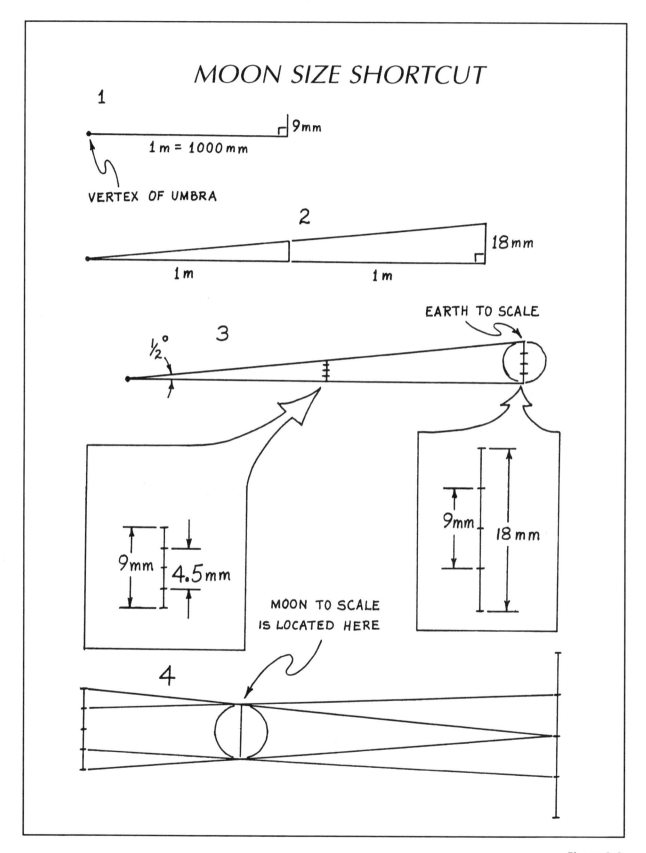

*MOON SIZE SHORTCUT*

1

9mm

1 m = 1000 mm

VERTEX OF UMBRA

2

18 mm

1 m          1 m

3          EARTH TO SCALE

½°

9mm   4.5mm

9mm   18 mm

MOON TO SCALE
IS LOCATED HERE

4

Figure 3-3

## Problem 2

Approximately how far does the moon travel in orbiting Earth once? Given that it takes the moon about 27 days to travel once around Earth, how fast is the moon moving relative to Earth?

## Puzzle

Each time you fold a piece of paper in half, the resulting folio is twice as thick as before you folded it. How many times would you have to fold the paper so that the resulting stack would be thick enough to reach from Earth to the moon? Assume that the paper is 0.1 mm thick.

## Report

Prepare an oral report on Hipparchus of Nicaea and how he used parallax to find the distance to the moon.

# ANGULAR DIAMETER
## Worksheet 3A

You have seen that both the sun and the moon have angular
  diameters of about 1/2 degree.
An angle measuring 1/2 degree runs diagonally across this page.
Let us call X the separation in centimeters between the
  rays forming the angle.
Call Y the distance in centimeters from the vertex to
  the point at which X is measured.

VERTEX
OF ANGLE

Select some point at random and measure

  $X_1$ and $Y_1$ :  $X_1 =$ _____  $Y_1 =$ _____

Compute $Y_1/X_1$ :

Choose another point and measure

  $X_2$ and $Y_2$ :  $X_2 =$ _____  $Y_2 =$ _____

Compute $Y_2/X_2$ :

Class average value for
  Y/X:

Clearly, whatever the size of the
moon ($D_M$) and its distance from
the earth ($L_M$) turn out to be, the
following proportion is true:

$$\frac{L_M}{D_M} = \frac{Y}{X}$$

If $D_M$ were 1,000 km, what would $L_M$ be?

If $L_M$ were 50,000 km, what would $D_M$ be?

If $D_M$ were 3,000 km, what would $L_M$ be?

If $L_M$ were 500,000 km, what would $D_M$ be?

# EARTH'S SHADOW IN SPACE
## Worksheet 3B

In order to understand what happens during a lunar eclipse, you need to know what kind of a shadow Earth casts in space. Figure 1 shows a small light bulb and a larger ball.

1. Draw in the shadow the ball will cast when the bulb is turned on.

LIGHT BULB                    BALL

Can you visualize the shape of the shadow in three dimensions? It should look like part of a cone with the sharp point removed.

2. Where is the vertex (point) of the cone located?

3. Since the sun is larger than Earth, what sort of shadow does Earth cast?

SUN                           EARTH

4. Draw in the shadow cast by Earth in question 3. Three tiny parts of the sun, A, B, and C, have been indicated. If you need help, sketch the shadows created by each of these pieces of the sun. Shade in on your drawing just those parts of the shadow that get no light from any part of the sun.

5. The part of the shadow that is in complete darkness is called the *umbra*. What shape would the umbra be in three dimensions?

   Where is its vertex?

6. The region in space that is partly in shadow is called the *penumbra*. This is the region that is in the shadow of parts, but not all, of the sun. What shape is the penumbra? Where is its vertex?

7. A lunar eclipse occurs when the moon enters Earth's umbra or penumbra. Because the penumbra is not completely dark, it is hardly noticeable when the moon enters it; but if any part of the moon enters the umbra you can see a very definite darkening on the moon. What phase must the moon be in for a lunar eclipse to occur?

8. Why don't we have lunar eclipses every month?

![shooting star logo]

# *LUNAR ECLIPSE*
## **Worksheet 3C**

1. Estimate the size of the moon's disk.

   Diameter of best trial disk:

   _____

2. Compute the diameter of the moon's disk.

   a. Draw a straight line connecting the tips of the image.

   b. Find the perpendicular bisector of this segment.

   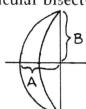

   c. Measure A and B:

   d. Compute the diameter of the moon's image:

   $$D_M = \frac{A^2 + B^2}{A}$$

   A = _____

   B = _____

   $D_M$ = _____

3. Estimate the size of Earth's shadow.

   Diameter of best trial disk:

   _____

4. Compute the diameter of Earth's shadow.

   a. Measure X and Y:

   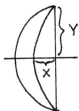

   X = _____

   Y = _____

   b. Compute the diameter of the shadow image:

   $$D_S = \frac{X^2 + Y^2}{X}$$

   $D_S$ = _____

5. Compute the ratio of shadow diameter to moon diameter:

   $$D_S / D_M$$

   _____

# THE MOON'S SIZE AND DISTANCE
## Worksheet 3D

Moon's angular diameter: _____

Sun's angular diameter: _____

Earth's diameter (circumference/$\pi$ ): _____

Ratio of Earth shadow diameter to moon diameter $D_S/D_M$ : _____

Ratio of moon distance to moon diameter $L_M/D_M$ :

Measure D and L from the drawing:  D = _____   L = _____

D represents Earth's diameter. $\triangle$ ACF represents Earth's shadow in space, $\triangle$ GBE the possible sizes and distances of the moon. To be a scale drawing, $\angle$GBE would have to measure 1/2°, but such a drawing would not fit on the page.

Find the actual length of Earth's shadow in space ($L_E$). Use the figures given above for Earth's diameter and the ratio $L_M/D_M$ : _____

We need to find $\ell$ such that $D_S/D_M$ will equal our computed value.

Will $\ell$ be less than 1/2 L or greater than 1/2 L? _____

Find $\ell$ by trial and error: _____

Compute $\ell$:

$$\ell = \frac{L}{1 + \frac{D_S}{D_M}}$$

_____

Compute the ratio $\ell/L$.                                    _____

This ratio, $\ell/L$, will hold even when ∠GBF is really 1/2°.

Compute the distance to the moon using the ratio $\ell/L$
and the length of Earth's shadow in space:         _____

Find the actual diameter of the moon:                  _____

# THE MOON'S SIZE AND DISTANCE 2
## Worksheet 3E

**Materials:** Adding machine tape
Long straightedge, such as an 8-foot length of 1" x 2" pine
Metric ruler
Drawing compass

**Overview:** You are going to make a scale drawing of Earth and the moon in space during a lunar eclipse. By using what you already know about Earth and the moon, you can make a drawing in which the moon will automatically appear of the right size and at the right distance from Earth.

Before you begin, you need to know the following things:

- the moon's angular size
- the sun's angular size
- the size of the moon compared to Earth's umbra during a total lunar eclipse
- Earth's size

**Procedure:**

1. Start by drawing Earth's umbra. Because the sun is so far from Earth and so much larger in size, the vertex angle of Earth's umbra is almost the same size as the sun's angular extent as viewed from Earth. On your adding machine tape, pick a point for the umbra's vertex and draw this angle. Extend the rays of your angle as far as you want, then draw a circle to represent Earth. See the illustration below.

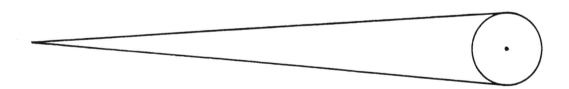

2. Inside the umbra draw the possible sizes of the moon. To do this, draw a vertical diameter through your Earth circle and measure its length. Compute the size of the moon relative to this and mark that distance on your diameter, centering it top to bottom. Then connect these marks to the vertex. See the illustration.

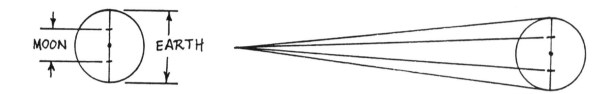

From your work with the photograph of a lunar eclipse you know that the moon is a certain fraction of the diameter of the umbra at the distance of the moon. The inner rays on your drawing show the possible sizes and distances of the moon.

3. You know also the angle the moon subtends when viewed from Earth. This angle also gives you possible sizes and distances. Construct this angle with its vertex at Earth's center. See the illustration below.

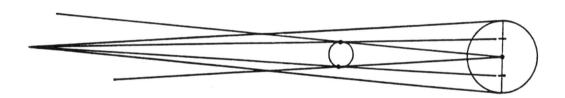

The points where these rays you've just drawn cross the others show you the only size and distance the moon could be to fulfill both sets of conditions. Draw a circle to represent the moon, with these two points on opposite sides of it. Why couldn't the moon be larger than this? Why couldn't it be smaller? Why couldn't it be located closer to or farther away from Earth than this?

4. Measure the moon's size and distance compared to Earth's diameter. Then use Earth's actual size to find the moon's actual size and distance from the scale drawing you have made. Record your results on "Our Neighborhood in Space."

# CHAPTER 4

## The Sun's Size
## and Distance from Earth

In this chapter you will measure the angular separation of the sun and moon in order to discover the distance between Earth and the sun.

## Background

In his pioneering work entitled *On the Sizes and Distances of the Sun and Moon,* Aristarchus gave the world two geometric methods for finding astronomical sizes and distances. We used the eclipse diagram in the last chapter; here we consider his other method, the lunar dichotomy.

In theory, the idea is simple and elegant. When the moon is at first or third quarter phase, the angle from sun to moon to Earth is exactly 90 degrees. Precisely at this time we measure the angle between the sun and the moon as seen from Earth. If the sun were infinitely far away, this angle would also be 90 degrees. Since the distance to the sun is not infinite, this angle will be less than 90 degrees and we can deduce the distance to the sun from this angle.

Unfortunately, in reality the method is difficult to apply. First, because the sun is roughly 400 times as far away as the moon, the angle we must measure differs from a right angle by only 1/7 of one degree. With our crude apparatus it will be quite challenging to measure the angle with sufficient exactitude.

Further, there will be problems in timing the observation. To see why, you need to know that the moon's synodic period (the time it takes to cycle through all of its phases, or to orbit all the way around Earth in relation to the sun) is about 29.5 days. Round this off to 30 days and see that the moon moves in its orbit about 12 degrees per day (360/30) or about 1/2 degree per hour!

The result is that, in order to get decent results, your observation must be made within a few minutes of the precise moment of first or last quarter phase. If you are 17 minutes too early, the distance you compute will be about half the true value; 17 minutes too late and the distance will appear to be infinite. In addition, the moment of first or third quarter phase for any given month may well come at a time when the sun or moon or both are below your horizon.

In spite of all these problems, the situation is not hopeless. Just realize that the results will be very crude, even by the standards established by the earlier activities. Be content if students discover that the sun is much farther away than the moon, on the order of many millions of miles. Aristarchus himself is said to have estimated the distance to the sun at 20 times that of the moon, whereas it is really about 400 times as great.

# Preparation

## Materials

Cardboard boxes, 30 cm x 30 cm x 60 cm or larger
Straight pins
Protractors
Straightedges or rulers

Choose some dates for this activity based on what time of day your classes meet. If you want to do it in the morning, select some days around the moon's third quarter phase; to do it in the afternoon select the first quarter phase. It is not necessary to do it exactly at the time of the precise phase, or even on the same day. A few days on either side will work. Refer to the *Nautical Almanac,* available at your local public library, or to the current issue of *Sky and Telescope* or *Astronomy* to help you find the best dates.

# The Distance to the Sun

Worksheet 4A, "How Far Away Is the Sun?" (pages 71–73) takes the students through the procedure. The idea is to measure the angular separation between the sun and the moon. Making this measurement on two or more occasions separated by hours or days allows the students to compute the moon's synodic period for themselves. Be advised that the period they find will be crude because the moon's angular velocity is not constant, since its orbit is not perfectly circular.

Finding the separation angle of the sun and moon is probably the most difficult task in this book. One student must hold the box and ensure that two of the straight pins stay lined up on the sun while another student tries to line up two more pins on the moon. What makes it difficult is that after the first two pins are lined up with the sun, the second student will at first probably not be able to line up the other pins with the moon because they won't all be in the same plane. The first student will then have to reorient the box, possibly several times, before the second student can complete the task. It is exacting work.

## The Size of the Sun

Knowing roughly the distance to the sun, we can find its actual size from its angular diameter measured from Earth. Worksheet 4B, "The Size of the Sun" (page 74), takes students through this exercise.

## Further Explorations

### Problem

How far does Earth travel in one orbit about the sun? What is Earth's average speed relative to the sun?

### Report

Prepare an oral report on Aristarchus of Samos. What is known of his life and accomplishments? Why is he sometimes called the ancient Copernicus?

### Project

The distance to the sun can be estimated even when the moon is not near first or third quarter by generalizing Aristarchus' method. See "Aristarchus Generalized" (figure 4-1). Call angle T the terminator angle. Measure angle E and sketch or photograph the moon at the same time. Then use worksheet 4C, "Moon Phase Angles" (page 75), and your sketch to find T. Then, use E and T and the known distance to the moon to find the distance to the sun.

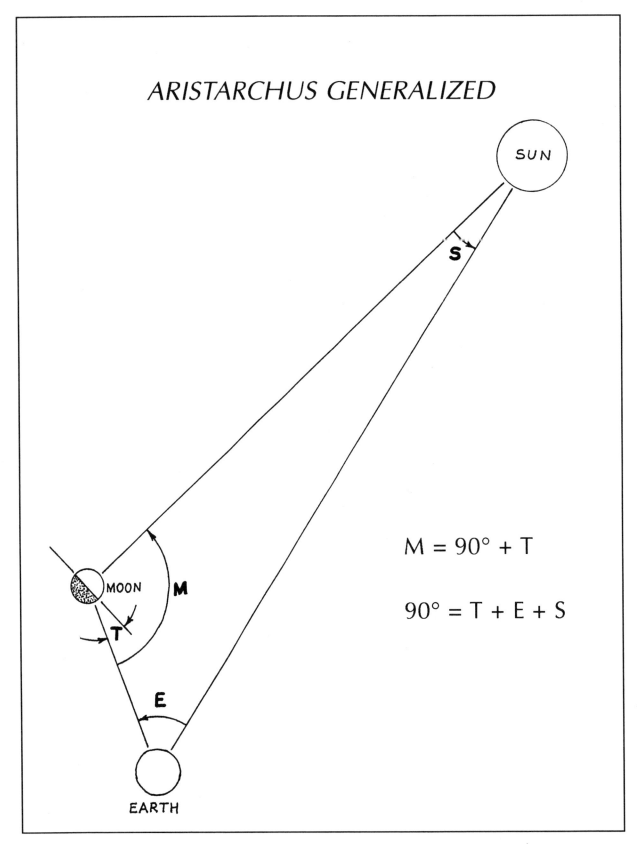

Figure 4-1

# *HOW FAR AWAY IS THE SUN?*
## Worksheet 4A

**Materials:**

> Flat piece of cardboard
> Four straight pins
> Protractor
> Straightedge

**Overview:**

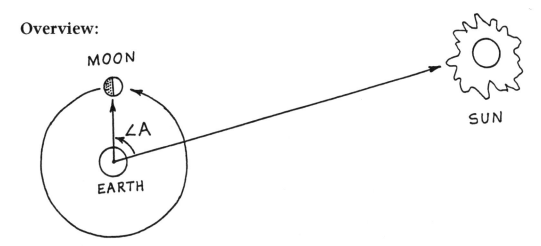

To help find the distance to the sun, measure the angle between the sun and the moon, angle A, as seen from Earth.

**Procedure:**

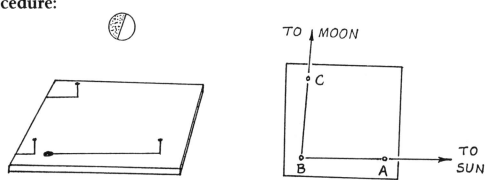

1. Set up your apparatus by placing two of the pins into the cardboard near one edge. Call these pins A and B. Take your materials outside to a place where you can see both the sun and the moon. **NEVER LOOK DIRECTLY AT THE SUN!**

Hold up the cardboard so that the two pins are lined up toward the sun. Do this by allowing the shadow of pin A to fall toward pin B.

While one member of your team holds the cardboard in this position, the second member is to place a third pin, C, so that line BC points toward the moon. Try this several times until pins B and C are lined up on the moon's terminator.

Record the date and time of your observation on the cardboard. **NEVER LOOK DIRECTLY AT THE SUN!**

2. Use your straightedge to construct lines AB and BC. Then measure angle ABC as precisely as you can and record that result on the cardboard also. Estimate your error. Now put your materials in a safe place until tomorrow. If you have to remove the pins from the cardboard, mark the holes so that you can replace the pins in the same spots later.

3. Repeat steps 1 and 2 each day as directed by your teacher. Leave pins A and B in the same position every time, but you may have to move pin C each day.

4. Record your data on the chart below.

| DATE | TIME | ANGLE | DIFFERENCE IN ANGLE | DIFFERENCE IN TIME (min.) |
|------|------|-------|---------------------|---------------------------|
|      |      |       |                     |                           |
|      |      |       |                     |                           |
|      |      |       |                     |                           |
|      |      |       |                     |                           |

**Analysis:**

1. Find the moon's angular velocity in degrees per minute. Hint: Angular velocity = change in angle / time between observations

2. At this rate, how long would it take for the moon to travel 360 degrees? This time is called the moon's synodic period.

3. How does this compare with the accepted value for the synodic period?

4. How would you explain any difference?

5. Get the exact time of the moon's quarter phase from your teacher. Using the moon's angular velocity you found above, compute the angle between the sun and the moon at that time.

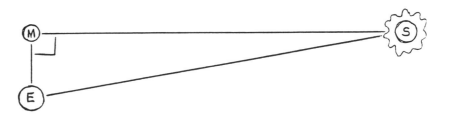

6. The drawing above represents the sun, Earth, and the moon when the moon is at first quarter phase. At that moment, angle EMS is a right angle. What did you find for the measure of angle MES? What must the measure of angle ESM be?

7. Can the measure of angle MES be more than 90 degrees? Why or why not?

8. If you found angle MES to measure more than 90 degrees, what may have been the cause of this?

9. Assuming maximum error in your readings, what is the smallest value that angle MES could have?

10. How can you find the distance to the sun if you know the distance to the moon and angle MES?

11. What is the largest value that the measure of angle MES could have? What would be the distance to the sun if angle MES had this value?

12. What is the smallest possible distance to the sun based on your answer to question 9?

# *THE SIZE OF THE SUN*
## Worksheet 4B

Distance from Earth to sun: _____

From Earth, the angular diameter of the sun is about 1/2 degree. Use the 1/2 degree angle displayed on this page to find the ratio of the sun's distance from Earth to the sun's diameter:

$$\frac{\text{Distance}}{\text{Diameter}} =$$

Now find the sun's diameter:

_____

VERTEX
OF ANGLE

Sun's radius: _____

Sun's circumference: _____

Sun's surface area ( $4\pi r^2$ ): _____

Sun's volume ( $\frac{4}{3}\pi r^3$ ): _____

Sun's diameter = How many Earth diameters? _____

If the sun were hollow, how many Earths would fit inside? _____

# MOON PHASE ANGLES
## Worksheet 4C

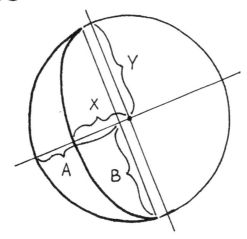

1. Guess the angle of the terminator: _____

2. Compute this angle:

    a. Draw a straight line connecting the cusps.

    b. Find the perpendicular bisector of this line segment.

    c. Measure A and B:

$$A = \underline{\hspace{2cm}} \qquad B = \underline{\hspace{2cm}}$$

    d. Compute R, the radius of the moon's image, from this formula:

$$R = \frac{A^2 + B^2}{2A} \qquad R = \underline{\hspace{2cm}}$$

    e. Find the center of the moon's image and construct the rest of the circle.

    f. Construct a diameter parallel to the line through the cusps.

    g. Measure X and Y:

$$X = \underline{\hspace{2cm}} \qquad Y = \underline{\hspace{2cm}}$$

    h. Find the angle of the terminator from X and Y:

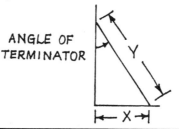

# CHAPTER 5

# The Distances to the Stars

This chapter uses the brightnesses of stars to suggest how far away they are. The solar system is placed in its proper context within a whole galaxy of stars.

## Background

In the previous chapters we looked at some of what can be learned from the direction of starlight; here we will consider what we can discover from its intensity.

Hipparchus was first to create a scale for judging the brightnesses of stars, and today's astronomers continue to use a version of his system. Stars are classified using a scale of magnitudes in which the brightest stars have the lowest numbered magnitudes; so, for example, a first magnitude star is brighter than a star of second magnitude.

At least since the time of Isaac Newton (1642–1727) it has been known that the stars are suns. That their enormous fiery expanses appear as mere pinpoints in an otherwise black sky proves that they must be very, very far away.

If we assume that all the stars in the night sky are just like our sun, then their differing brightnesses may simply be the result of their differing distances from us. How brightness varies with distance is described by the inverse square law, which says that the apparent brightness of an object in space diminishes by the square of its distance.

Christian Huygens (1629–1695), Dutch astronomer and contemporary of Newton, applied the inverse square law to estimate the distance to Sirius, the brightest star in the night sky. His method is simple to understand. From a darkened room he observed the sun through a hole, which he made smaller and smaller until he judged the resulting brightness to equal that of Sirius at night. If this brightness were 1/144 of the brightness of the full sun, for example, then Sirius could be 12 times as far away as the sun, since 12 squared is 144. Actually, Sirius's brightness is about one ten-billionth of the brightness of the sun, so this method would suggest that Sirius is about 1,000,000 times as far away as the sun.

In spite of its simple elegance, Huygens's procedure yields poor results because the assumption that other stars have intrinsically the same brightness as the sun is far from valid. Astronomers now know that stars can range from dwarfs with a small fraction of the sun's luminosity to giants many thousands of times as bright. The brightest stars visible in our sky tend to be these intrinsically brilliant giants, so that they are actually much farther away than Huygens's method suggests. Still, the procedure does give a rough idea of typical stellar distances.

# Preparation

## Materials

16 candles
Photographic light meter
Adding machine tape
Plain white paper, 8 1/2" x 14" or larger
Box of salt
Rulers
Compasses

The demonstration to help the students discover the inverse square law of light intensity must be done in a large room that can be completely darkened.

## Inverse Square Law

All students need to have copies of worksheet 5A, "How Does Distance Affect Brightness?" (pages 80–81). Place one candle on a metal pie plate or other nonflammable tray and light it. Darken the room and have a student hold the light meter near the candle to get a measurable reading on the meter. Have another student measure the distance from candle to meter and call this distance one unit.

The student with the meter should then move back from the candle until he or she is 2 units away. The students now predict how many candles will be needed on the tray to give the same reading on the light meter as before. After all have recorded their predictions, add candles to the tray, placing them near the first candle, until the readings are almost the same. Record the results.

Have the student with the meter move to 3 units away and repeat the procedure. Then, if possible, try it 4 units away. By this time reflected light from the walls may begin to interfere.

After this demonstration the students should finish the worksheet on their own.

## Distances to the Stars

After a class discussion to make sure everyone understands the inverse square law of light intensity, the student teams should be able to complete worksheet 5B, "Distances to the Stars" (pages 82–83). This has the students compute distances to certain stars given their measured brightnesses compared to the sun by applying the inverse square law. It also introduces the idea of the light year as a unit of distance.

## Putting It All Together

Worksheet 5C, "Putting It All Together" (page 84), asks students to put together everything they have learned about sizes and distances in the local part of the galaxy.

## Our Galaxy of Stars

To put our solar system into proper perspective, worksheet 5D, "Stars in Our Galaxy" (page 85), has the students visualize a scale model of the Milky Way using salt grains to represent individual stars.

# HOW DOES DISTANCE AFFECT BRIGHTNESS?

## Worksheet 5A

| Distance (1 unit = ___cm) | Predicted Number of Candles | Actual Number of Candles |
|---|---|---|
| 1 unit | _____ | _____ |
| 2 units | _____ | _____ |
| 3 | _____ | _____ |
| 4 | _____ | _____ |
| 5 | _____ | _____ |
| 6 | _____ | _____ |
| 10 | _____ | _____ |
| n | _____ | _____ |

How is the needed number of candles related to distance?

Given the following distances, find the number of candles needed to provide the same amount of light as that provided by one candle at a distance of one unit:

8 units _____ candles

100 units _____ candles

2.5 units _____ candles

Given the following numbers of candles, find the distances at which they will provide the same amount of light as that provided by one candle at a distance of one unit:

_____ units 49 candles

_____ units 121 candles

_____ units 400 candles

_____ units 2 candles

_____ units 3 candles

_____ units 8 candles

_____ units n candles

80

If the intensity of one candle at a distance of one unit is defined to be 1, what will be the intensity of that one candle at these distances?

| Distance | Intensity |
|----------|-----------|
| 2 units | _____ |
| 3 units | _____ |
| 4 units | _____ |
| 10 units | _____ |
| n units | _____ |

What will be the distance if the intensity of one candle is as follows:

| Distance | Intensity |
|----------|-----------|
| _____ units | 1/25 |
| _____ units | 1/10,000 |
| _____ units | 1/144 |
| _____ units | 0.0004 |
| _____ units | 1/2 |
| _____ units | 1/3 |
| _____ units | 1/n |

Extra Credit:

| Distance | Intensity |
|----------|-----------|
| _____ units | 2/5 |
| _____ units | 3/8 |
| _____ units | a/b |

# DISTANCES TO THE STARS
## Worksheet 5B

Our sun is a fairly typical star. If it were as far away as the stars you see at night, it would appear no brighter than they. We can use this fact to get rough estimates of the distances to the stars. We will assume, for the purpose of this exercise, that all stars have the same intrinsic brightness as the sun. How reasonable is this assumption?

The sun can be thought of as a single candle and the distance from Earth to the sun represents one unit. The brightest star in the sky at night is the star called Sirius, the Dog Star, known to astronomers as Alpha Canis Majoris because it is the brightest star in the constellation of Canis Major. The observed brightness of Sirius is one ten-billionth of the sun's brightness. How far do you estimate it is to Sirius?

_____ units = _____ miles

Actually, astrophysicists have determined that if placed next to the sun, Sirius would be 25 times as bright as the sun. What does this tell you about the distance to Sirius? What is your new estimate of the distance?

_____ units = _____ miles

The dimmest stars we can see with the unaided eye appear about 1/900 as bright as Sirius. How far away do you estimate them to be?

_____ units = _____ miles

The dimmest stars that can be seen with the 200-inch Hale telescope at Mt. Palomar appear about $10^{-10}$ or one ten-billionth as bright as Sirius. How far away do you estimate them to be?

_____ units = _____ miles

82

The numbers of miles you have found are inconveniently large. To avoid these large numbers astronomers often use a unit of distance called the *light year*. A light year is defined as the distance that light travels in a year. Light travels at about 186,000 miles per second. Therefore:

one light second = _____ miles

one light minute = _____ miles

one light hour = _____ miles

one light day = _____ miles

one light year = _____ miles

Rounded off to the nearest trillion miles,

one light year _____ miles

How long does it take light from the sun to reach Earth?

How long would it take a laser beam to reach the moon?

Convert the distances to the stars that you computed above into light years:

Distance to Sirius = _____ light years

Distance to the dimmest naked-eye stars = _____ light years

Distance to the dimmest stars seen with a telescope = _____ light years

An alien civilization living on a planet 40 light years from Earth listens for radio signals from other planets. If they were able to pick up radio waves from Earth, what would they hear? (Note: Radio waves travel at the speed of light.)

# PUTTING IT ALL TOGETHER
## Worksheet 5C

1. On a piece of adding machine tape, draw Earth and the moon to scale at the right scale distance apart.

2. On a piece of legal size paper, draw circles whose diameters are in proportion to those of the sun, Earth, and the moon.

3. On the other side of the paper, show the distance to the moon and the distance to the sun on the same scale. What is the diameter of the sun to the same scale? Draw in the sun. What is the diameter of Earth to the same scale? Can you draw it in?

4. The nearest star to the sun is Proxima Centauri, which lies about four light years away in the direction of the constellation called the Centaur. To visualize this distance in terms of things we have already found, do this:

   a. Round off the distance from Earth to the sun to the nearest 100 million miles:

      Distance to sun = _____ miles

   b. Rename 4 light years into miles (1 l.y. = 6 trillion miles)

      4 light years = _____ miles

   c. The distance to Proxima Centauri is how many times as far as the distance from Earth to the sun?

      Distance to Proxima Centauri = _____
      times the distance to the sun

5. On a piece of paper draw a line segment 1 cm long. This will represent the distance from Earth to the sun. At one end of the line segment make a very tiny dot. This will represent the sun. Almost surely you will have made the dot too large, since to this scale the sun would have a diameter of about 0.1 mm, or about the thickness of a sheet of paper.

   a. Proxima Centauri would be another tiny dot about how many centimeters away?

   b. How many meters is that?

6. Take the paper outside and see whether you can see a tree or a building that is about that far away. To help you visualize the vastness of interstellar space, remember that Proxima Centauri is the nearest star to the sun; all of the others are even farther away.

PI IN THE SKY © 1993 Zephyr Press, Tucson, AZ

# STARS IN OUR GALAXY
## Worksheet 5D

**Materials:** Box of table salt, metric rulers

1. Take a single grain of salt and measure its length in cm. _____

2. Compute the volume of your grain of salt, assuming that it is cubical in shape. _____

3. Using the net weight listed on the box and the fact that the density of table salt is 2.165 g/cc, calculate about how many grains of salt are in the whole box. (Hint: Divide the total weight by the density to find the total volume of salt in the box; then divide the total volume by the volume of a single grain.) (1 oz. = 28.35 g) _____

The Milky Way that you may have seen at night when you have been far from city lights is actually our galaxy. A galaxy is an enormous group of stars, gas, and dust held together by gravity. The Milky Way galaxy is disk shaped, flat like a plate, but thicker in the center and consisting of spiral arms. The sun is an average star located about two-thirds of the way out from the center in one of the spiral arms. The Milky Way is only one of millions of galaxies in the universe.

4. Our galaxy contains about 200 billion stars. If each grain of salt in the box represents one star, how many boxes of salt would we have to spill on the floor to represent all the stars in our galaxy? _____

5. Try to visualize that many boxes of salt. Would they fit into the trunk of a car? The back of a pickup truck? A railroad boxcar? What could carry them? _____

6. How far apart should the salt grains be spaced to represent the stars to scale? To find out, let the length of your salt grain represent the diameter of the sun. What scale factor is this? (Hint: The sun's diameter is about $1.4 \times 10^{11}$ cm.) _____

7. What is the distance from Earth to the sun on the same scale? (The actual distance is about $1.5 \times 10^{13}$ cm.) _____

8. How far away is the nearest star at the same scale? (The actual distance is about $4.0 \times 10^{18}$ cm.) _____

So, to make a scale model of our galaxy using salt, you would need a trainload of salt and you would have to place the individual grains of salt eight or nine miles apart to represent the individual stars!

# APPENDIX A

# Glossary of Astronomical Terms

**Altitude:** The angular distance of a celestial object above the observer's horizon. Altitude and azimuth together completely specify an object's location on the dome of the sky.

**Apparent Solar Time:** Sundial time. To find the local mean time, add the equation of time to sundial time.

**Azimuth:** The horizontal angle between the direction in question and a chosen initial direction, usually due north. For a celestial object, the azimuth is measured from the north point of the horizon clockwise to the foot of the object's vertical circle. Altitude and azimuth together completely specify an object's location on the dome of the sky.

**Celestial Equator:** A great circle on the celestial sphere halfway between the north and south celestial poles. It represents a projection or extension of Earth's equator.

**Celestial Pole:** A projection of one of Earth's poles onto the celestial sphere; a point on the dome of the sky directly above one of Earth's poles.

**Celestial Sphere:** The dome of the sky. We can imagine celestial objects being located on a sphere of enormous radius, centered on Earth.

**Circumpolar:** Describing stars that never set. Viewed from anywhere except Earth's equator, one of the celestial poles is above the horizon and stars near it appear to travel in circular paths around it as Earth turns.

**Culmination:** The moment when a celestial object crosses the observer's meridian.

**Cusp:** Either one of the points of a crescent moon.

**Declination:** The angle between a celestial object and the celestial equator; the celestial equivalent of latitude. Declination and right ascension together completely specify the location of an object on the celestial sphere.

**Ecliptic:** The plane of Earth's orbit projected onto the celestial sphere. On a map of the stars, it is also the apparent path of the sun through the course of a year.

**Equation of Time:** The correction to be applied to local apparent time, or sundial time, to find the local mean time. It is necessary because the sun's apparent motion is not quite uniform throughout the year.

**Equinox:** (1) Either of two points on the celestial sphere where the ecliptic intersects the celestial equator. (2) Either of two times of the year when the sun crosses the celestial equator.

**First Point of Aries:** The point of zero right ascension, defined as the point where the sun crosses the celestial equator at the time of the vernal or spring equinox.

**Greenwich Mean Time (G.M.T.):** Mean solar time computed at the longitude of Greenwich, defined as the hour angle of the mean sun measured at Greenwich.

**Gnomon:** An object that casts a shadow used as an indicator.

**Horizon:** The circular intersection of a plane tangent to the Earth at the observer's location with the celestial sphere.

**Hour Angle:** The angle from an observer's celestial meridian to the hour circle of a celestial object, measured westward along the celestial equator.

**Hour Circle:** A great circle on the celestial sphere that passes through the poles and intersects the celestial equator at right angles.

**Latitude:** Angular distance north or south of the Earth's equator.

**Limb:** The extreme edge of the visible disk of a star, planet, or satellite.

**Local Mean Time:** Mean solar time for a given location.

**Longitude:** The angular distance on Earth measured east or west of the meridian that passes through Greenwich, called the prime meridian.

**Mean Solar Time:** Time measured with reference to the mean sun, having equal twenty-four-hour days throughout the year.

**Mean Sun:** A fictitious sun defined as moving at a uniform rate along the celestial equator so as to complete its orbit in the same period as the apparent sun.

**Meridian:** (1) A great circle on the Earth's surface passing through both poles and through an observer's location. (2) A great circle on the celestial sphere passing through both celestial poles and through an observer's zenith. This is also called the celestial meridian.

**Meridian Transit:** The movement of an object across an observer's celestial meridian.

**Nadir:** The point on the celestial sphere directly below the observer's position; the direction of the pull of gravity

**Normal:** (1) Perpendicular, at right angles. (2) A line that is perpendicular to something else.

**Obliquity:** The angle between the planes of the celestial equator and the ecliptic. It is also the tilt of Earth's axis with respect to the normal to the plane of Earth's orbit.

**Revolve:** To orbit a central point. Usually the point is outside the revolving object.

**Right Ascension:** The angle, measured eastward along the celestial equator, from the vernal equinox to the hour circle of a celestial object. It is the celestial equivalent of longitude. Declination and right ascension together completely specify the location of an object on the celestial sphere.

**Rotate:** To turn or spin on an axis. Usually the axis is inside the rotating object.

**Sidereal:** Having to do with the stars.

**Sidereal Day:** The time required for Earth to rotate once on its axis compared to the background of stars. A star in a given spot in the sky will reach the same spot again exactly one sidereal day later. Since Earth is orbiting the sun at the same time as it is spinning on its axis, the sun will not be in exactly the same location after one sidereal day. A sidereal day is about 23 hours, 56 minutes, 4 seconds long in units of mean solar time.

**Solar Day:** The time interval between two successive meridian passages of the sun.

**Solstice:** (1) Either of two times of the year when the sun is at the most northern or most southern points of the ecliptic. (2) Position of the sun on the celestial sphere when it is farthest north (summer solstice) or farthest south (winter solstice).

**Synodic Period:** The time needed for a celestial body to complete a cycle from a specified position relative to the sun and Earth back to the same relative position.

**Terminator:** The dividing line between the lighted and shaded parts of the disk of the moon or a planet.

**Transit:** (1) The movement of a small celestial body in front of a larger one. (2) The passage of a celestial body across the observer's meridian.

**Universal Time (U.T.):** Greenwich Mean Time, defined as the hour angle of the mean sun measured at Greenwich.

**Vernal Equinox:** (1) The point where the ecliptic intersects the celestial equator as the sun is moving north. (2) The time when the sun crosses the celestial equator as it moves north.

**Vertical Circle:** An arc of a great circle drawn on the celestial sphere through one's zenith and a celestial object that meets the horizon at right angles.

**Zenith:** The point on the celestial sphere that is directly overhead.

**Zenith Angle:** The angle between a celestial object and the observer's zenith.

**Zone Time:** The mean solar time figured at the central meridian of each of the twenty-four time zones.

# APPENDIX B

# Pursuing an Interest in Astronomy

If these activities have kindled or rekindled an interest in astronomy in you or your students, then you may be wondering what to do next. Opportunities for the amateur enthusiast to explore the universe are unlimited, from reading about the latest discoveries to casual observing to serious observing programs whose data will be used by professional astronomers. There is a bewildering array of resources to aid you in these endeavors, but much of it is unknown or confusing to the beginner. This section consists of some advice on where to begin for someone just getting started in astronomy.

Do *not* buy a telescope yet. An amateur's telescope will not let you see the spectacular color shots of planets, nebulae, and galaxies that are so common in the glossy magazines. Those photos are generally long time exposures taken with large, professional telescopes or from spacecraft. You can see—and photograph for yourself—some remarkable things, but you will first need to learn how to use a telescope and what you can expect from the many different types of equipment available. To do this you should join a local astronomy club, attend the star parties, and learn all you can about the members' scopes.

If you need to buy something, buy a comfortable, portable, reclining lawn chair. Then, far from smog and city lights, set it up under a sparkling sky, get comfortable, and watch. You will be able to learn the constellations, watch the changing phases of the moon, see the planets wander among the stars, witness unexpected meteors, and contemplate the expanding cosmos. Later, you may want to purchase a good pair of binoculars to extend your vision. To keep up with events in astronomy—both occurrences in the heavens and the latest progress in science—you will want to read the periodical literature. *Astronomy* is an excellent magazine for beginners, and *Sky and Telescope* is often the choice of the more serious observer. The Astronomical Society of the Pacific offers a free quarterly newsletter for teachers called *The Universe in the Classroom*; all you have to do is request it on school letterhead. The addresses for all of these periodicals are listed in the Bibliography.

You will want to read some books to learn more about basic astronomy. There are so many available that it may be hard to know where to start. A good place to begin is with Terence Dickinson's *Nightwatch* (see Bibliography for publisher of this and other books). This book is highly readable and contains much basic knowledge of astronomy along with excellent star charts and advice for amateurs.

To follow *Nightwatch*, you could do no better than Guy Ottewell's *The Astronomical Companion*. This slender, large-format volume is very inexpensive and is absolutely packed with a tremendous amount of information, much of which is never found in standard textbooks. Ottewell has drawn a series of highly imaginative sketches unlike any you will see elsewhere, which are designed to put the structure of the universe into perspective.

After *The Astronomical Companion* you will have to make a choice. Those interested primarily in observing will need something like the *Observer's Handbook* for the current year from the Royal Astronomical Society of Canada, which lists the basic data for events in the solar system for the year, and a guidebook like Sherrod's *A Complete Manual of Amateur Astronomy*, which suggests projects for amateurs. Those more interested in theory may want to turn next to Moche's *Astronomy* or Kaufmann's *Universe,* both good introductions.

For younger readers, say under age eighteen, and teachers of these children, outstanding explication of astronomical concepts is provided by Isaac Asimov, well-known science fiction author and popularizer of science. *The Double Planet, The Clock We Live On,* and *Alpha Centauri: The Nearest Star* are three good choices to begin with. Youngsters should also be given opportunities to attend planetarium shows; I remember many happy hours as a child at San Francisco's Morrison Planetarium.

Start tonight by going outside and looking at the sky. Our Earth is a giant spaceship streaking through the cold vacuum of interstellar space. We are fortunate in being able to look through a nearly transparent atmosphere—the window of our spaceship—toward the stars, nebulae, and galaxies that populate our universe. You will surely find, as most amateur enthusiasts of my acquaintance have found, that observing the heavens is more than a hobby—it is a spiritual experience.

# APPENDIX C
# Derivation of Formulas

## SUN COMPASS DIMENSIONS

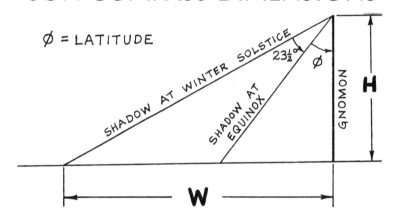

Ø = LATITUDE

SHADOW AT WINTER SOLSTICE

SHADOW AT EQUINOX

23½°

Ø

GNOMON

H

W

The sun compass described in these activities has a gnomon erected near its southern edge and has a table width equal to twice the gnomon's height. This arrangement works well if your latitude is between 20 and 40 degrees. Near the equator, the gnomon would be better situated in the middle of the table. Above 40 degrees north latitude (or below 40 degrees south latitude) the gnomon height (H) and the table width (W) will work better with a different ratio. You can compute the maximum table width you will need from the following relationship:

**W = H tan (LATITUDE + 23 1/2°)**

This table summarizes very workable values of H and W:

| YOUR LATITUDE | RELATIONSHIP |
|:---:|:---:|
| **UP TO 40°** | **W = 2H** |
| **UP TO 48°** | **W = 3H** |
| **UP TO 55°** | **W = 5H** |

# FINDING THE RADIUS
# GIVEN A CIRCULAR ARC

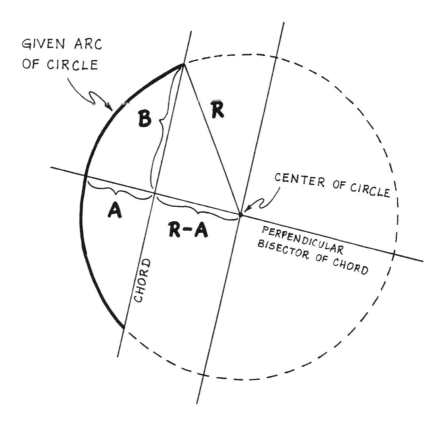

*From Triangle:*

$$R^2 = (R-A)^2 + B^2$$

$$= R^2 - 2AR + A^2 + B^2$$

$$\Rightarrow 2AR = A^2 + B^2$$

$$R = \frac{A^2 + B^2}{2A}$$

# SHADOW CONE ANGLE

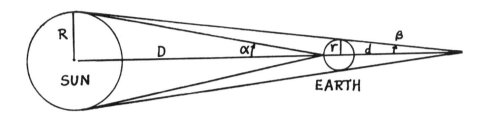

Because the sun is larger than Earth, the shadow cast by Earth forms a cone in space which points away from the sun. Light rays from the sun striking the eye of an observer on Earth also form a cone. We want to show that this cone and the Earth's shadow cone have nearly identical vertex angles, shown as $\angle \alpha$ and $\angle \beta$ in the drawing above.

$$\tan \alpha = \frac{R}{D}$$

$$\tan \beta = \frac{R}{D+d} = \frac{r}{d}$$

Since $\frac{R}{D+d} = \frac{r}{d}$, we can solve for $d$ to find

$$d = \frac{D}{\frac{R}{r} - 1}$$

$$= \frac{rD}{R-r}$$

Now $\tan \beta = \frac{r}{d} = \frac{r(R-r)}{rD} = \frac{R-r}{D} \approx \frac{R}{D}$

since $r$ (about 4,000 miles) is small compared to $R$ (about 430,000 miles)

# LUNAR DISTANCE FORMULA

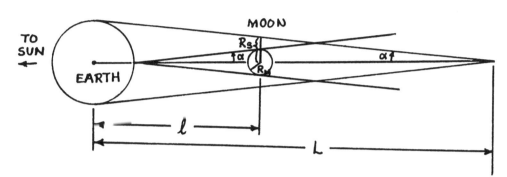

$\ell$ = distance to moon

$L$ = length of Earth's shadow cone

$R_M$ = radius of moon

$R_S$ = radius of shadow cone at moon's distance

$\alpha$ = angular radius of moon

$\alpha \approx$ vertex angle of shadow cone (see Shadow Cone Angle)

$$\tan \alpha \approx \frac{R_M}{\ell} \quad \text{and} \quad \tan \alpha = \frac{R_S}{L-\ell} \quad \text{so}$$

$$\frac{R_M}{\ell} = \frac{R_S}{L-\ell} \quad \Rightarrow \quad \frac{L-\ell}{\ell} = \frac{R_S}{R_M}$$

$$\frac{L}{\ell} = \frac{R_S}{R_M} + 1$$

$$\ell = \frac{L}{\dfrac{R_S}{R_M} + 1}$$

# APPENDIX D
# Answer Key

## Introduction

1. Earth rotates in a counterclockwise direction when viewed from over the north pole.
2. The celestial equator meets your horizon due east and due west of you, rather than south of these points, because the radius of the celestial sphere is essentially infinite (see figure 3).
3. The declination of Polaris is very nearly 90 degrees. Actually, it's about 89.03 degrees.
4. The declination of a star that passes through your zenith will equal your latitude on Earth.
5. One hour of longitude corresponds to 15 degrees, since Earth turns about 360 degrees in 24 hours and 360/24 = 15.
6. Viewed from far above Earth's north pole, Earth would revolve counterclockwise in its orbit around the sun.
7. Since Earth travels 360 degrees around the sun in 365.25 days, the sun moves along the ecliptic an amount equal to 360 degrees divided by 365.25 days, or about one degree per day.

## Chapter 1: Astronomical Angles

### Angles, Size, and Distance

1. The diameters in the photo are the same.
2. No.
3. The smallest ball is closer to the camera; the largest is farther away.
4. In figure B they are all the same distance away. In figure C, the golf ball is closest, the basketball farthest away.

5. The angle subtended by his head, as measured at my eye, got smaller as he moved away.
6. The tree will appear bigger in photograph D because it subtends a larger angle at the camera here than in photo E.
7. Ant a, 70 degrees; ant b, 105 degrees. The pencil looks larger to ant b.
8. 140 degrees.
9. Measured from a point midway between eraser and writing tip, the distance is one-half the pencil's length. Younger students will measure perpendicular to the axis of the pencil; more advanced students may discover that the ant can be located anywhere along the circle whose diameter the pencil defines.
10. As the ant gets closer and closer, the angle approaches 180 degrees. It reaches 180 degrees if the ant's eye touches the pencil.
11. As the ant gets farther away, the angle approaches 0 degrees. It won't be exactly 0 until the ant is infinitely far away.
12. The tree should be twice as large in the photo from 10 meters; half as large in the photo from 40 meters.

# Angular Size of the Sun

## Overview

1. It would have subtended a smaller angle than it does today.
2. No, because you must not look directly at the sun.
3. Answers will vary.

## Procedure

2c. The image moves because the sun appears to move across the sky. The students need to know that this motion is a result of Earth's rotation.
2d. The image should move one image diameter in about 2 minutes.
2e. Most students think the image size will increase, but it won't. The image stays the same size but becomes brighter.
2f. Covering half of the hole gives the hole a D shape. The students are usually surprised to find that the image does not change shape but instead becomes fainter, since less light gets through the hole.
3a. Answers vary.
3b. Angle S measures about one-half degree.
3c. 24 hours.
3d. About 2 minutes. This is 1/720 of a day, since there are 1,440 minutes in a day ($24 \times 60 = 1440$).
3e. 1/720 of 360 degrees = 1/2 degree.
3f. The two answers should agree closely; both methods show the sun's angular extent to be one-half degree.

# Chapter 2: The Size of Earth

## Further Explorations

1. Answers vary.

### Problem 1

Computing as shown below, the radius turns out to be 4,067 miles.

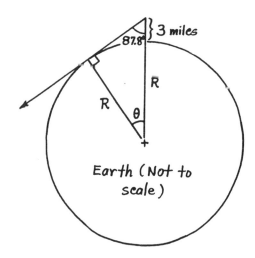

$$m\angle\theta = 2.2°$$

$$\cos 2.2° = \frac{R}{R+3} \quad\Rightarrow\quad 1 + \frac{3}{R} = \frac{1}{\cos 2.2°}$$

$$\frac{3}{R} = \frac{1}{\cos 2.2°} - 1$$

$$R = \frac{3}{\left(\frac{1}{\cos 2.2°} - 1\right)}$$

$$R = \frac{3\cos 2.2°}{1 - \cos 2.2°}$$

$$R \approx 4067 \text{ miles}$$

This solution ignores the effect of refraction of light by the Earth's atmosphere.

### Problem 2

Using 4,000 miles for Earth's radius, the ship will be about 4 miles away when the hull just disappears.

Since $\theta$ is small, about 0.06°, the distance from the observer to the ship is essentially equal to X.

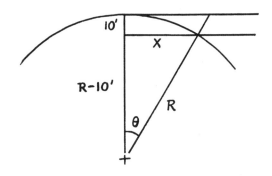

$$R = 4000 \text{ miles}$$
$$= 21,120,000 \text{ feet}$$

$$(R-10)^2 + X^2 = R^2 \quad\Rightarrow\quad X^2 = 20R - 100$$
$$= 20(R-5)$$

$$\therefore \quad X = \sqrt{20(R-5)}$$
$$= 2\sqrt{5(R-5)}$$
$$\approx 20,552 \text{ feet}$$
$$\approx 4 \text{ miles}$$

This solution also ignores the effect of refraction.

## Problem 3

Taking Earth's circumference as 25,000 miles, one could walk nonstop for:

12,500 hours or 521 days at 2 miles per hour

8,333 hours or 347 days at 3 miles per hour

6,250 hours or 260 days at 4 miles per hour

Slightly more realistically, one could walk at a rate of 2 miles per hour for 8 hours each day. The trek would then take 1,562.5 days or about 4.3 years.

## Problem 4

(a) Yes, near the poles. If you could walk 10 miles in a day, for instance, you could march in a circle about 1.5 miles in radius around the north or south pole.

(b) About 1,042 miles per hour, since it would have to fly 25,000 miles in 24 hours.

(c) About 1,048 miles per hour, since it would now have to fly about 25,145 miles in 24 hours.

(d) At a latitude of about 55 degrees north or 55 degrees south.

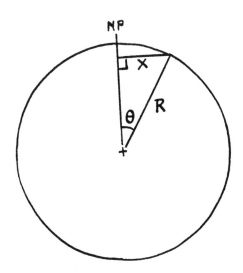

The distance traveled on Earth's surface is $2\pi X$

$600 \text{ mph} \times 24 \text{ hrs.} = 14,400 \text{ miles}$

$2\pi X = 14,400 \Rightarrow X = \dfrac{14,400}{2\pi}$

$\approx 2,292 \text{ miles}$

Now $\sin\theta = \dfrac{X}{R} \Rightarrow \theta = \arcsin\dfrac{X}{R}$

$= \arcsin 0.573$

$\approx 35°$

Latitude $= 90° - \theta \approx 55°N$ or $55°S$

(e) About 800 miles per hour. Since the latitude of New York is 41 degrees north and that of San Francisco is 38 degrees north, it would have to be able to fly about 19,252 miles in 24 hours.

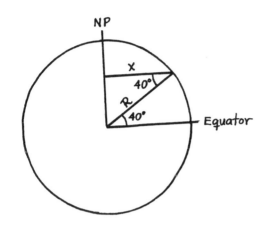

For a latitude that is about 40° N ...

$$\frac{X}{R} = \cos 40° \Rightarrow X = R \cos 40°$$
$$\approx 3064 \text{ miles}$$

The necessary speed then becomes

$$\text{Speed} = \frac{2\pi X}{24 \text{ hrs.}}$$
$$= \frac{2\pi \cdot 3064}{24} \text{ mph}$$
$$\approx 800 \text{ mph}$$

**Puzzle 1**

About 1.9 inches. This old puzzle always amazes those who encounter it for the first time. Everyone assumes that because the Earth is so large the addition of one foot to the girdle would make no noticeable difference. Actually, the size of the spherical body on which you try this is irrelevant. The girdle will stand off from the surface about 1.9 inches regardless of the size of the ball. Try it with a golf ball and a basketball.

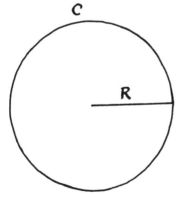

$$2\pi R = C$$

If C is increased by one foot, the radius will also increase. Call the new radius $R'$ (R prime):

$$2\pi R' = C + 1$$
$$R' = \frac{C+1}{2\pi}$$
$$= \frac{C}{2\pi} + \frac{1 \text{ ft.}}{2\pi}$$
$$= R + \frac{1 \text{ ft.}}{2\pi}$$
$$\approx R + 1.9 \text{ inches}$$

**Puzzle 2**

(a) It froze. This is a variation on the old chestnut that goes something like this: A hunter hiked 2 miles south from his campsite, then hiked one mile west. Here he shot a bear and dragged it back to his campsite, 2 miles due north. What color was the bear? (White) My version is not an improvement, but a more complicated story to try on students who already know the standard version.

(b) The campsite may have been at the north pole. The path the man took does not bring him back to his campsite unless he started there, or—

(c) He could have been very near the south pole. Try those directions starting from a point 1.318 miles from the south pole. In this case he walks one mile south toward the pole and then by going east he walks in a circle around the pole back to where he turned, and finally walks north to his starting point. Actually, his starting point could be anywhere on a circle of radius 1 plus $1/(N \times pi)$ miles, where N is any counting number and the circle is centered on the south pole. N tells you how many times the man circles the pole in his walk.

## Puzzle 3

(a) She was going to Bermuda. Perth (latitude 32 degrees south, longitude 115 degrees east) and Bermuda (latitude 32 degrees north, longitude 65 degrees west) are nearly exactly opposite each other on Earth. To fly from one to the other you could go along any great circle, just as from the north pole to the south pole you could fly along any circle of longitude.

(b) Any two places that are opposite each other on Earth. Finding two cities or other named spots is not easy. Here are a few that work or almost work:

North pole to south pole

Honolulu (21 N, 158 W) to eastern Angola (21 S, 22 E)

Buenos Aires (34 S, 58 W) to Shanghai (31 N, 121 E)

Singapore (1 N, 104 E) to Quito, Ecuador (0 S, 78 W)

Djakarta, Indonesia (6 S, 107 E) to Bogota, Colombia (4 N, 74 W)

## Project

Answers vary. Diameter = Circumference/Pi. Scale example: If the globe is 18 inches in diameter, then, taking 8,000 miles as the actual diameter, the scale is

$$18 \text{ inches}/8,000 \text{ miles} = 18 \text{ in.}/(8,000 \times 5,280 \times 12 \text{ in.})$$
$$= 1/28,160,000$$

The difference in elevation between the highest peak (29,000 feet) and the deepest ocean trench (-38,000 feet) is about 67,000 feet. To this scale, that difference would be

$$67,000 \text{ feet}/28,160,000 = 0.0024 \text{ feet}$$
$$= 0.03 \text{ inches}$$
or a little less than 1/32 inch!

## Earth and Sun

1. Answers vary.
2. The boundary between the lighted and dark parts.
3. About one-half.
4. The part lighted by the sun experiences day, the rest night.
5. Sunrise and sunset are experienced along the terminator.
6. Earth rotates counterclockwise.
7. East is the direction the Earth turns.
8. 360 degrees in 24 hours; 180 degrees in 12; 90 degrees in 6.
9. About 12 hours from sunrise to sunset; 6 from sunrise to noon
10. 15 degrees per hour, since 360/24 = 15.
11. Earth revolves counterclockwise.
12. One year, about 365.2422 days.
13. The point on Earth directly below the sun. On Earth at this point the sun is directly overhead and a vertical pole would cast no shadow.
14. It is local apparent noon. It is also local apparent noon all along the meridian of longitude that goes through the subsolar point.
15. It points north if you are north of the subsolar point; it points south if you are south of this point.
16. When the shadow of a vertical pole is shortest for that day, the time is local apparent noon.
17. When the shadow of a vertical pole is shortest for that day, the shadow points toward true north (if you are north of the subsolar point).
18. The shadow travels from west to east.
19. The sun appears to travel from east to west, due to the turning of Earth from west to east.
20. Answers vary, but not too much. Students should draw Earth orbiting the sun in a counterclockwise direction, spinning counterclockwise as it does so.

# Chapter 3:
# The Moon's Size and Distance from Earth

## Further Explorations

### Problem 1

(a) Since the distance to the moon is about 240,000 miles, you could walk there nonstop in about 14 years at 2 miles per hour. Going a more realistic 10 miles per day, it would take you 24,000 days or about 66 years.

(b) 4,800 hours or 200 days.

(c) 120 hours or 5 days.

### Problem 2

The moon travels about $2 \times$ pi $\times$ radius or $2 \times 3.14 \times 238,000$ miles = 1,500,000 miles in going once around Earth. Since it takes the moon 27.3 days to do this, it moves at about 55,000 miles per day or 2,300 miles per hour relative to Earth.

### Puzzle

42 times. Have the students guess before they compute it; they will almost certainly overestimate. The distance to the moon is about 384,000,000 meters (238,000 miles). Fold as follows:

| Fold | Thickness | Fold | Thickness | |
|------|-----------|------|-----------|---|
| 0 | 0.1 mm | 21 | 210 | meters |
| 1 | .2 | 22 | 419 | (rounded) |
| 2 | .4 | 23 | 839 | |
| 3 | .8 | 24 | 1,678 | |
| 4 | 1.6 | 25 | 3,355 | |
| 5 | 3.2 | 26 | 6,711 | |
| 6 | 6.4 | 27 | 13,422 | |
| 7 | 12.8 | 28 | 26,843 | |
| 8 | 25.6 | 29 | 53,687 | |
| 9 | 51.2 | 30 | 107,374 | |
| 10 | 102.4 | 31 | 214,748 | |
| 11 | 204.8 | 32 | 429,497 | |
| 12 | 409.6 | 33 | 858,993 | |
| 13 | 819.2 | 34 | 1,717,987 | |
| 14 | 1,638.4 mm | 35 | 3,435,974 | |
| | =1.6384 meters | 36 | 6,871,948 | |
| 15 | 3.2768 m | 37 | 13,743,895 | |
| 16 | 6.5536 | 38 | 27,487,791 | |
| 17 | 13.1072 | 39 | 54,975,581 | |
| 18 | 26.2144 | 40 | 109,951,162 | |
| 19 | 52.4288 | 41 | 219,902,324 | |
| 20 | 104.8576 | 42 | 439,804,648 | |

Since you obviously cannot fold a piece of paper this many times, ask the students what would happen if you cut it in half and stacked the pieces. After 42 cuts and stacks the stack of paper would be high enough to reach the moon. How big would the individual pieces of paper be?

## Angular Diameter

Y/X should be about 115/1.
If $D_M$ is 1,000 km, then $L_M$ is 115,000 km.
If $L_M$ is 50,000 km, then $D_M$ is about 435 km. If D is 3,000 km, then $L_M$ is 345,000 km.
If $L_M$ is 500,000 km, then $D_M$ is about 4,348 km.

## Earth's Shadow in Space

1.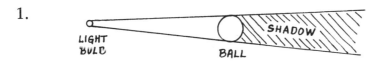

2. The vertex of the cone is at the light bulb.
3. Answers vary.

4.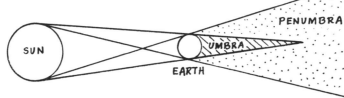

5. The umbra is another cone, this time pointing away from Earth. The vertex is in space on the opposite side of Earth from the sun.
6. The penumbra is a cone with its vertex in space between the sun and Earth.
7. The moon must be full for a lunar eclipse to occur.
8. Because usually the moon passes above or below the Earth's umbra.

## Lunar Eclipse

The ratio of shadow diameter to moon diameter should be about 2.7/1 or about 8/3.

## The Moon's Size and Distance

These results are needed to complete worksheet 3D:

- the moon's angular size is about 1/2 degree
- the sun's angular size is about 1/2 degree
- the moon's diameter is about 0.37 or 3/8 of the diameter of Earth's umbra at its distance away
- the Earth's diameter is about 8,000 miles
- Students should find that the moon's diameter is about 1/4 of the Earth's diameter and that it is located about 30 Earth diameters away from our world.

# Chapter 4:
# The Sun's Size and Distance from Earth

## Further Explorations

1. Since the distance to the sun is about 93,000,000 miles, the distance around the sun is about 584,000,000 miles. Covering this distance in 365 days means going 1,600,000 miles per day or about 67,000 miles per hour.

## How Far Away Is the Sun?

1. The moon cycles through all of its phases in 29.5 days, on average, so the angular velocity computed should be around 0.5 degree per hour or 0.008 degree per minute.
2. About 30 days.
3. The accepted value for the synodic period is 29.5 days.
4. The moon's angular velocity is not constant because its orbit is elliptical, not circular.
5. The angle should be 89.85 degrees, but students are doing well if they get anything in the range of 80 to 100 degrees.
6. Angle ESM measures very close to zero degrees.
7. No, because the sum of the angles of a plane triangle is 180 degrees.
8. Experimental error.
9. Answers vary.
10. Make a scale drawing and use similar triangles, or use trigonometry.
11. Angle MES would have a maximum value of 90 degrees if the distance to the sun were infinite.
12. Answers vary.

## The Size of the Sun

Distance from Earth to sun is about 93,000,000 miles.
Ratio of distance to diameter is about 115/1.
Therefore the sun's diameter is roughly 810,000 miles
Radius is 405,000 miles
Circumference is 2,500,000 miles
Surface area is 2,000,000,000,000 (2 trillion) square miles
Volume is 300,000,000,000,000,000 (300 quadrillion) cubic miles
Diameter is about 100 Earth diameters
The sun's volume would accommodate about one million Earths.

# Chapter 5: The Distances to the Stars

## How Does Distance Affect Brightness?

| Distance | Actual Number of Candles |
|---|---|
| 1 unit | 1 |
| 2 units | 4 |
| 3 | 9 |
| 4 | 16 |
| 5 | 25 |
| 6 | 36 |
| 10 | 100 |
| n | $n \times n$ or n squared |
| 8 | 64 |
| 100 | 10,000. |
| 2.5 | 6.25 |
| 7 | 49 |
| 11 | 121 |
| 20 | 400 |
| 1.414 | 2 |
| 1.732 | 3 |
| 2.828 | 8 |
| square root of n | n |

| Distance | Intensity | Distance | Intensity |
|---|---|---|---|
| 2 units | 1/4 | 5 units | 1/25 |
| 3 | 1/9 | 100 | 1/10,000 |
| 4 | 1/16 | 12 | 1/144 |
| 10 | 1/100 | 50 | 0.0004 |
| n | 1/n squared | 1.414 | 1/2 |
| | | 1.732 | 1/3 |
| | | $\sqrt{n}$ | 1/n |
| | | $\sqrt{5/2}$ | 2/5 |
| | | $\sqrt{8/3}$ | 3/8 |
| | | $\sqrt{b/a}$ | a/b |

# Distances to the Stars

The assumption that all stars have the same intrinsic brightness is not even close, but it does give us a starting point to get some ball park ideas of distances.

If Sirius is one-ten-billionth as bright as the sun, then we would expect it to be the square root of ten billion times as far away as the sun, or 100,000 times the distance to the sun; that's about 9,300,000,000,000 (9.3 trillion) miles.

If Sirius is intrinsically 25 times as bright as the sun, then we expect it to be the square root of 25 (5) times as far away. That means our new estimate is 500,000 times the distance to the sun or 46.5 trillion miles away.

The dimmest naked-eye stars must be 30 times as far away as Sirius, about 15 million Astronomical Units (the distance to the sun is one Astronomical Unit) or 1.4 quadrillion miles away.

The dimmest stars visible with a telescope must be 100,000 times as far away as Sirius, about 50 billion Astronomical Units or 4.7 quintillion miles away.

One light second = 186,000 miles
One light minute = 11,160,000 miles
One light hour = 669,600,000 miles
One light day = 16,070,400,000 miles
One light year = 5,865,696,000,000 miles
Or about 6,000,000,000,000 (6 trillion) miles

For light to reach Earth from the sun takes about 8.3 minutes.

For a laser beam to reach the moon takes about 1.29 seconds.

Distance to Sirius is about 8 light years.

Distance to dimmest naked-eye stars is about 230 light years.

Distance to dimmest visible stars is about 775,000 light years.

The aliens would hear radio programs from the 1950s (if you are reading this in the 1990s).

## Putting It All Together

1, 2, 3. Check the students' drawings.

4a.     100,000,000 (100 million) miles

4b.     24,000,000,000,000 (24 trillion) miles

4c.     240,000 times

5a.     240,000 cm

5b.     2,400 m = 2.4 km or about 1.5 miles

## Stars in Our Galaxy

1.   Answers vary; typically 0.5 mm = 0.05 cm

2.   0.000125 cubic cm

3.   Typical net weight 737 g (26 oz.)

     Total volume in box = 737 g/2.165 g per cc = 340 cubic cm

     Number of salt crystals = 340 cc/0.000125 cc = 2,720,000

4.   200 billion stars/2,720,000 salt crystals per box = 73,529 boxes of salt

5.   One cubic meter = 1,000,000 cubic cm

     Volume of typical box is 800 to 1,000 cubic cm, so 73,500 boxes would require 59 to 74 cubic meters. This is clearly too large for a car or pickup truck. A railroad boxcar might just work.

6.   0.05/140,000,000,000,000  =  0.000000000000357

7.   15,000,000,000,000 cm $\times$ 0.000000000000357  =  5.355 cm

8.   4,000,000,000,000,000,000 cm * 0.000000000000357

     = 1,428,000 cm = 14,280 m

     = 14.28 km

     = 8.87 miles

# BIBLIOGRAPHY

## Basic Astronomy

Asimov, Isaac. *Alpha Centauri, The Nearest Star.* New York: William Morrow & Company, 1976.

———. *Asimov on Astronomy.* New York: Bonanza Books, 1974.

———. *The Clock We Live On.* New York: Abelard-Schuman, 1959.

———. *The Double Planet.* New York: Abelard-Schuman, 1966.

———. *The Sun Shines Bright.* Garden City, N.Y.: Doubleday, Inc., 1981.

Baker, Robert H. *Astronomy.* 8th ed. Princeton, N.J.: D. Van Nostrand, 1964.

Haysham, H. *Basic Astronomy.* London: Thomas Reed, 1971.

Hoyle, Fred. *Astronomy.* Garden City, N.Y.: Doubleday, 1962.

Johnson, Willis E. *Mathematical Geography.* New York: American Book Company, 1907.

Kaufmann, William J., III. *Universe.* New York: W. H. Freeman, 1988.

Moche, Dinah L. *Astronomy.* 3d ed. New York: John Wiley & Sons, 1987.

Motz, Lloyd, and Anneta Duveen. *Essentials of Astronomy.* Belmont, Calif.: Wadsworth, 1966.

Ronan, Colin A. *The Practical Astronomer.* New York: Bonanza Books, 1984.

## Historical Astronomy

Ferris, Timothy. *Coming of Age in the Milky Way.* New York: William Morrow, 1988.

Hawkins, Gerald S. *Beyond Stonehenge.* New York: Harper and Row, 1973.

———. *Stonehenge Decoded.* Garden City, N.Y.: Doubleday, 1965.

Heath, Sir Thomas. *Aristarchus of Samos: The Ancient Copernicus.* New York: Dover, 1981.

Krupp, E. C. *Echoes of the Ancient Skies.* New York: Harper and Row, 1983.
Neugebauer, O. *The Exact Sciences in Antiquity.* New York: Dover, 1969.
Van Helden, Albert. *Measuring the Universe: Cosmic Dimensions from Aristarchus to Halley.* Chicago: University of Chicago Press, 1985.

## Mathematical Astronomy

Beet, E. A. *Mathematical Astronomy for Amateurs.* New York: W. W. Norton & Co., 1972.
Smart, W. M. *Text-Book on Spherical Astronomy.* Cambridge: Cambridge University Press, 1965.

## Astronomical Calculations

Burgess, Eric. *Celestial Basic: Astronomy on Your Computer.* Berkeley, Calif.: SYBEX, 1982.
Duffett-Smith, Peter. *Practical Astronomy with Your Calculator.* Cambridge: Cambridge University Press, 1983.
Mills, H. R. *Positional Astronomy and Astro-Navigation Made Easy.* New York: John Wiley & Sons, 1978.
*Space Mathematics: A Resource for Teachers.* Washington, D.C.: National Aeronautics and Space Administration, 1972.

## Astronomical Projects

Alter, Dinsmore. *Introduction to Practical Astronomy.* New York: Thomas Y. Crowell, 1933.
Engelbrektson, Sune, and Peter Greenleaf. *Let's Explore Outer Space.* New York: Sentinel Books, 1969.
Graves, Richard. *Bushcraft.* New York: Schocken, 1972.
Johnson, Gaylord, and Irving Adler. *Discover the Stars.* New York: Arco, 1975.
Knox, Richard. *Experiments in Astronomy for Amateurs.* New York: St. Martin's Press, 1976.
Schaaf, Fred. *Seeing the Sky.* New York: John Wiley & Sons, 1990.
———. *Seeing the Solar System.* New York: John Wiley & Sons, 1991.
Sherrod, P. Clay. *A Complete Manual of Amateur Astronomy.* Englewood Cliffs, N.J.: Prentice-Hall, 1981.
Tattersfield, D. *Projects and Demonstrations in Astronomy.* New York: John Wiley & Sons, 1979.
Waxman, Jerry. *A Workbook for Astronomy.* Cambridge: Cambridge University Press, 1984.

## Observation Aids

Bishop, Roy L., ed. *Observer's Handbook 1992*. Toronto: The Royal Astronomical Society of Canada, 1991.

Dickinson, Terence. *Nightwatch: An Equinox Guide to Viewing the Universe*. Camden East, Ontario: Camden House, 1983.

Harrington, Philip S. *Touring the Universe through Binoculars*. New York: John Wiley & Sons, 1990.

Martin, Martha E., and Donald H. Menzel. *The Friendly Stars*. New York: Dover, 1966.

Menzel, Donald H. *A Field Guide to the Stars and Planets*. Boston: Houghton Mifflin, 1964.

Norton, Arthur P., and J. Gall Inglis. *Norton's Star Atlas and Telescopic Handbook*. Cambridge, Mass.: Sky Publishing, 1966.

Ottewell, Guy. *Astronomical Calendar 1992*. Greenville, S.C.: Astronomical Workshop, Furman University, 1991.

————. *The Astronomical Companion*. Greenville, S.C.: Astronomical Workshop, Furman University, 1979.

Sidgwick, J. B. *Observational Astronomy for Amateurs*. 2 vols. New York: Dover, 1971.

## Fiction

Harness, Charles L. "Summer Solstice," in *Terry Carr's Best Science Fiction of the Year*. New York: Tom Doherty Associates, 1985.

## Periodicals

*Astronomy*, published monthly by Kalmbach Publishing Company, 625 E. St. Paul Avenue, P.O. Box 92788, Milwaukee, Wisconsin, 53202.

*Mercury*, published bimonthly by the Astronomical Society of the Pacific, 390 Ashton Avenue, San Francisco, California, 94112.

*Sky & Telescope*, published monthly by Sky Publishing Corporation, 49 Bay State Road, Cambridge, Massachusetts, 02238-1290.